A Strategic Guide to Continuing Professional
Development for Health and Care Professionals:
The TRAMm Model

Full the full range of M&K Publishing books please visit our website:
www.mkupdate.co.uk

A Strategic Guide to Continuing Professional Development for Health and Care Professionals:
The TRAMm Model

Deb Hearle
Sarah Lawson
Roe Morris

A Strategic Guide to Continuing Professional Development for Health and Care Professionals:
THE TRAMm Model

Deb Hearle, Sarah Lawson & Roe Morris

ISBN: 9781905539-72-7

First published 2016

British Library Cataloguing in Publication Data
A catalogue record for this book is available from the British Library

Notice

Clinical practice and medical knowledge constantly evolve. Standard safety precautions must be followed, but, as knowledge is broadened by research, changes in practice, treatment and drug therapy may become necessary or appropriate. Readers must check the most current product information provided by the manufacturer of each drug to be administered and verify the dosages and correct administration, as well as contraindications. It is the responsibility of the practitioner, utilising the experience and knowledge of the patient, to determine dosages and the best treatment for each individual patient. Any brands mentioned in this book are as examples only and are not endorsed by the publisher. Neither the publisher nor the authors assume any liability for any injury and/or damage to persons or property arising from this publication.

Disclaimer

M&K Publishing cannot accept responsibility for the contents of any linked website or online resource. The existence of a link does not imply any endorsement or recommendation of the organisation or the information or views which may be expressed in any linked website or online resource. We cannot guarantee that these links will operate consistently and we have no control over the availability of linked pages.

To contact M&K Publishing write to:
M&K Update Ltd · The Old Bakery · St. John's Street
Keswick · Cumbria CA12 5AS
Tel: 01768 773030 · Fax: 01768 781099
publishing@mkupdate.co.uk
www.mkupdate.co.uk

Designed and typeset by Mary Blood
Printed in Scotland by Bell & Bain

Contents

List of tables

List of figures

About the authors

Deb Hearle

Senior Lecturer and Associate Director Undergraduate Studies (Allied Health Professions) Cardiff University; MSc Interprofessional Studies (Health), Dip COT, PGCE (HE), FHEA, Dip ISM

Deb is an occupational therapist and an experienced educator and manager. She has been teaching both undergraduate and postgraduate healthcare students for over 20 years, including aspects of professional development. She runs study days and postgraduate courses, which contribute to CPD. She also accredits professional courses alongside the Health and Care Professions Council, where CPD is a requirement. She has mentored the TRAMm design team from the outset of the project. More recently, she has joined the core TRAMm development group. Deb is currently exploring the application of CPD as part of her doctoral studies.

Sarah Lawson

Community Occupational Therapist, Cheshire West and Chester Council; BSc (Hons) Occupational Therapy; BSc (Hons) Health and Social Welfare

Sarah has spent the last five years working in social services. In addition to taking a leading role on CPD development, she supervises local university students. Sarah joined the core TRAMmCPD development group in 2010 and she is the lead designer of TRAMm Tracker and TRAMm Trail. Sarah leads on website development as well as managing TRAMmCPD's social media presence.

Roe Morris

Practice Manager, Community Occupational Therapy Team, Cheshire West and Chester Council; BSc (Hons) Occupational Therapy

Roe was the co-ordinator of the original TRAMm model design team and is a member of the core TRAMmCPD development group. She has been an occupational therapist for six years and has worked in social services for the last 29 years. As well as being a community occupational therapist, Roe is responsible for the development and promotion of this role within the local authority. She supervises students from local universities, leads group and mentorship supervision for social care assessors and leads on CPD development within her workplace.

Preface

Continuing professional development (CPD) is an essential component of today's working practice for all professionals involved in health and social care. It is a core aspect of clinical governance and is closely linked with quality monitoring and improvement. Professional bodies have produced guidelines to support and direct the professional development of nurses and allied health professionals (AHPs 2003, RCN 2007) as well as social workers (TCSW 2015).

When there is significant investment in CPD (whether individually or via organisational policy), the individual feels valued and is happy in their work and their quality of practice is shown to improve (Van den Broeck *et al.* 2008, Schaufeli & Bakker 2004). In contrast, when CPD is given limited attention, this has been shown to correlate with work-related stress and burnout, resulting in increased staff sickness, absence and subsequent decreased productivity (Van den Broeck *et al.* 2008, Schaufeli & Bakker 2004). Although all health and social care staff are familiar with the term 'CPD' and are aware of its requirements, there are many different ideas of what constitutes CPD and the ways in which health professionals are expected to demonstrate their personal and professional development.

Since the introduction of the Health and Care Professions Council (formerly Health Professions Council) in 2002, the profile of CPD for allied health professionals has risen significantly. There are now many processes and procedures within the workplace that are designed not only to monitor and measure performance but also to identify training needs. Such processes include preceptorship, supervision, appraisal/professional development review and clinical audit. Health and care professionals are commonly expected to complete professional development portfolios and there is guidance available on how to record progress, including many examples of online portfolios. However, there is little explanation of the reasons for CPD or advice on how professionals can fully embrace it as an integral part of their practice, rather than as something that has to be done solely to meet professional and organisational requirements.

What is the purpose of this book?

There is a growing demand for knowledge specialisation and this requires health and care students and professionals to adopt varied and innovative approaches to learning (GeSCI 2009). This, together with the drive to embrace and integrate new technologies, helps to facilitate the engagement (rather than passive participation) of students and professionals in CPD. TRAMmCPD is a package that brings all these aspects of learning together. It provides a toolkit to encourage a more strategic approach to your personal and professional development. It consists of a model illustrating the requirements for evidencing successful CPD, and a set of tools to help you:

- Plan and record your activities
- Monitor and measure your progress
- Apply and disseminate your CPD.

After an introduction to CPD and a section helping you to identify your preferred learning styles, the book follows the stages (depicted as stations) of TRAMm namely: Tell (T), Record (R), Activity (A), Monitor (M) and Measure (m). It discusses their integration and application, illustrating the core principles and their application by means of a concurrent case study. Your own learning needs will provide the main focus, enabling you to develop a full profile that will meet the requirements of CPD as the chapters progress. At the end of each chapter, there are opportunities to reflect on your learning and apply theory to practice through questions and tasks.

Who is this book for?

As will become evident, this book is primarily (but not exclusively) aimed at those professionals registered with the Health and Care Professions Council (HCPC) who, as part of their biennial re-registration process, must undertake and evidence CPD. HCPC do not 'approve' particular CPD activities or CPD schemes but encourage registrants to use whatever they find helpful and relevant to their development. HCPC also provides its own structure to help you meet their standards (HCPC 2012a).

There are currently 330,887 people registered with the HCPC. These individuals come from 16 professional groups: arts therapists, biomedical scientists, chiropodists/podiatrists, clinical scientists, dieticians, hearing aid dispensers, occupational therapists, operating department practitioners, orthoptists, paramedics, physiotherapists, practitioner psychologists, prosthetists/orthotists, radiographers, social workers in England (see Chapter 1 for social care staff in the rest of the UK), and speech and language therapists.

This book is designed to be accessible for all levels, from health and care students to experienced practitioners. The text may also be useful for associated support workers and other healthcare professional groups who are also required to undertake CPD, such as doctors, pharmacists, optometrists, nurses and midwives. Some aspects of the book will also be useful for professionals outside the healthcare professions, who are required to undertake and evidence CPD.

The primary focus of this book is allied health professionals in the UK. However, some key issues presented will be relevant to other health and social care professionals or practitioners overseas. The handbook, although designed to build knowledge and skills by logical progression through each chapter, can also be utilised by accessing ad hoc chapters or sections as required.

Authors' note

At the time of writing, the government has announced the closure of the College of Social Work (TCSW). It is therefore anticipated that any guidance documents currently housed by the TCSW are liable to change in the near future.

What is continuing professional development (CPD) and why do we do it?

This chapter defines CPD and explains why it is important. It introduces the key professional requirements – particularly those of the Health and Care Professions Council (HCPC), which are discussed in depth. A brief overview of professional contacts in the UK is also presented, as well as some useful international links for anyone considering working outside, or coming to, the UK.

The chapter concludes by examining the potential impact of CPD on a person's personal and professional development and their practice. This will be illustrated with a case study (which will continue through all the chapters to illustrate the use of the model). There are also some tasks at the end of the chapter, to encourage you to consider the implications of the HCPC standards and professional CPD guidelines.

What is CPD?

The Allied Health Professions Project (2003, p. 9) defines CPD as

> 'a range of learning activities through which health professionals maintain and develop throughout their career to ensure that they retain their capacity to practise safely, effectively and legally within their evolving scope of practice'.

This definition has been adopted by the HCPC (2012a) for the purpose of regulation.

CPD is an ongoing process that usually begins as soon as an individual completes their qualification for their chosen career. In the field of health and social care, it applies to practitioners, educators, managers and researchers. In forward-thinking organisations, it can also be applied to any member of staff, including support, administrative, domestic and technical staff. In most health and social care professions, students are also encouraged to commence their CPD when they begin their course of study, by using and developing a professional portfolio (see Chapter 5). This helps them develop ways of planning and structuring CPD records for their future careers and lifelong learning.

The principles of CPD also apply to many professions outside healthcare, including teaching, surveying, engineering and the law. Each profession has its own CPD requirements, ranging from a mandatory course or minimum required CPD hours and/or CPD points to an outcome-based approach where the emphasis is on impact.

Many practitioners do not have a strategic personal development plan and the process and practice of CPD is often misunderstood. Some may attend workshops, courses or professional conferences (whether or not the learning fits their career and learning objectives), in the belief that they are thereby meeting their CPD obligations. For most professions, CPD can cover many types of learning – both formal and informal and increasingly involving the use of social media. However, it should always be undertaken in a considered way in order to be meaningful and meet its aims.

Why undertake CPD?

CPD: A mandatory responsibility

The term 'Continuing Professional Development' has been used for many years. However, until the introduction of clinical governance in the UK in 1998, it was not given much importance. Clinical governance was instigated in the National Health Service (NHS) in order to guide the improvement of practice (DH 1998). Scally and Donaldson (1998, p. 61) described it as 'a system through which NHS organisations are accountable for continuously improving the quality of their services and safeguarding high standards of care by creating an environment in which excellence in clinical care will flourish'.

Between 1990 and 1995, at the Bristol Royal Infirmary, 35 babies died unnecessarily and dozens were left brain damaged (DH 2002). The associated scandal provided the impetus for the introduction of clinical governance and the subsequent focus on CPD. In social care, cases such as those of Victoria Climbié in 2000 and Baby P in 2007 stimulated this discussion and led to the instigation of further quality assurance mechanisms. Before 1998, CPD was mostly undertaken by those who were motivated to develop themselves both personally and professionally. Those with lower aspirations could therefore hold back progress in service delivery. However, following the introduction of clinical governance, it was no longer acceptable for health professionals to refrain from further development after they had qualified. The need to continuously update knowledge and skills was elevated in status from desirable to expected (Starey 2001).

Scally and Donaldson (1998) highlighted the importance of organisations valuing employees and their professional development, as these employees would be the future leaders of change. They considered that if people in the organisation felt valued, they would strive to make the organisation successful by delivering a high-quality service that ultimately benefited those in their care. This was based on evidence from those deemed to be successful organisations and has, more recently, been supported by Strong (2009).

Despite changes in government and a continually changing NHS, the concept of clinical governance has remained. For this reason, the acknowledged value of CPD has continued to grow and it is now considered to be an important factor in quality improvement and a core responsibility of the health and social care professional. Today, all qualified health and social care staff are required to undertake CPD and, in many instances, it is a prerequisite for professional registration.

In the UK, health and social care mandatory requirements and standards are set by regulatory bodies, appointed by the government, such as the HCPC, the Nursing and Midwifery Council (NMC), the General Medical Council (GMC), or country-specific Care Councils. Specific requirements depend upon the particular professional group and in some cases (such as social care) these also differ across England, Northern Ireland, Scotland and Wales. For example, in Wales social care staff (apart from occupational therapists) register with the Care Council for Wales (CCW) and also need to provide evidence of CPD every three years. In Scotland the regulatory body is the Scottish Social Services Council (SSSC), and in Northern Ireland it is the Social Care Council (NISCC). A memorandum of understanding has been agreed between the HCPC and these respective Care Councils (collectively known as 'the Four Councils') to ensure the regulation of social workers and the approval of social work education across the UK. Within this regulation falls the responsibility of monitoring CPD, while individual professional bodies provide guidance on how CPD can be guided, supported and ensured.

CPD: A personal and professional responsibility

Although the mandatory requirements described above are of central importance, they are not the only reasons for undertaking CPD. Evidence also shows that we should all see CPD as an essential part of our working lives – for both personal and professional reasons.

Professional education programmes and codes of conduct emphasise our professional responsibility to provide the highest quality of care to service users, even in the absence of mandatory requirements. In order to do this, we must continually develop our skills, based on evidence regarding which interventions work well and which do not, or require special considerations for maximum impact. The NHS Staff Council (2009) found that staff who felt valued (through the provision of professional development opportunities) were likely to demonstrate increased levels of satisfaction and motivation and were therefore more likely to continue working for an organisation. This suggests that, when any CPD is undertaken, staff integrate their learning and skill acquisition into the organisation and help to develop high-quality care together. Another indirect, positive consequence of this is safer and more effective patient care (RCN 2007).

There are also health benefits from undertaking CPD. Strong et al. (2003) found that supervision, one method of facilitating CPD, can help to increase job satisfaction, effectiveness and clinical reasoning, while at the same time preventing stress and burnout (see Chapter 7). In organisations such as the NHS, there is a high prevalence of staff absence due to work-related stress

(HSE 2015). This suggests that individual and organisational investment in CPD can also help to reduce these potential health consequences of stress.

This book is written for all HCPC-registered professionals. The principles may apply to anyone who is interested in formalising their professional development, particularly those from healthcare backgrounds. The next section of this chapter will outline specific documented expectations for those registered by the HCPC.

How do you demonstrate CPD?

For allied health professionals (AHPs), regulation is undertaken by the HCPC, who stipulate that all AHPs *must* demonstrate CPD. At present, 16 professions are regulated by the HCPC (HCPC 2014a). Each one has its own professional body, which provides further support for CPD and has its own HCPC 'Standards of Proficiency'. These standards include some generic elements, which apply to all registrants, as well as some profession-specific elements. The Standards of Conduct, Performance and Ethics (HCPC 2012b) and the five Standards for CPD (HCPC 2012c) apply to all HCPC-regulated professions. The 16 professional groups and their websites are listed in Table 1.1.

Table 1.1 AHP professional bodies and website addresses

Profession	Professional body and website
Art therapists	British Association of Art Therapists *http://www.baat.org*
Biomedical scientists	Association of Biomedical Healthcare Scientists *https://www.ibms.org*
Chiropodists/Podiatrists	Society of Chiropodists and Podiatrists *http://www.scpod.org*
Clinical scientists	Association of Clinical Scientists *http://www.assclinsci.org/acsApplicants/acsBodies.aspx*
Dieticians	British Dietetic Association *https://www.bda.uk.com/*
Hearing aid dispensers	British Society of Hearing Aid Audiologists *http://www.bshaa.com*
Occupational therapists	British Association of Occupational Therapists and College of Occupational Therapists *https://www.cot.co.uk*
Operating department practitioners	College of Operating Department Practitioners *https://www.unison.org.uk/at-work/health-care/representing-you/unison-partnerships/codp/*

Orthoptists	British and Irish Orthoptic Society *http://www.orthoptics.org.uk*
Paramedics	College of Paramedics *https://www.collegeofparamedics.co.uk*
Physiotherapists	Chartered Society of Physiotherapy *http://www.csp.org.uk*
Practitioner psychologists	British Psychological Society *http://www.bps.org.uk*
Prosthetists/Orthotists	British Association of Prosthetists and Orthotists *http://www.bapo.com*
Radiographers (Diagnostic/Therapeutic)	College of Radiographers *http://www.sor.org*
Social Workers (England)*	British Association of Social Workers *https://www.basw.co.uk*
Speech and language therapists	Royal College of Speech and Language Therapists *http://www.rcslt.org*

In Wales social workers continue to be regulated by the Care Council for Wales. In Scotland this remains the responsibility of the Scottish Social Services Council, and in Northern Ireland it is the Northern Ireland Social Care Council. There is a memorandum of understanding between these regulators and the HCPC, and members can also register with the HCPC if they wish. For further details see: http://www.hcpc-uk.org.uk/ aboutregistration/regulators/socialwork/

The HCPC has developed a set of generic CPD standards for all allied health professions, which require registrants to record current and relevant activities and ensure learning is transferred into practice to benefit the service user (HCPC 2012c). Every time you renew your registration, you need to confirm that you continue to meet the following standards (HCPC 2012a, p. 4):

1. Maintain a continuous, up-to-date and accurate record of your CPD activities

2. Demonstrate that your CPD activities are a mixture of learning activities relevant to current or future practice

3. Seek to ensure that your CPD has contributed to the quality of your practice and service delivery

4. Seek to ensure that your CPD benefits the service user

5. Upon request, present a written profile (which must be your own work and supported by evidence) explaining how you have met the standards for CPD.

According to the HCPC (2012a, p. 6), this means the following:

1. You must keep a record of your CPD, in whatever format is most convenient for you (e.g. TRAMm Tracker and Trail).

2. You must make sure your CPD is a mixture of different kinds of activities – not just one kind of learning – and that it is relevant to your work. It could be relevant to your current role or to a planned future role or to the future direction of the organisation in which you work.

3. You should aim for your CPD to improve the quality of your work. This may not always be achieved (due to factors beyond your control) but you should always intend your CPD activities to influence and have a positive impact on your practice.

4. You should aim for your CPD to benefit service users; you may not be able to ensure that this happens every time, but you should have the intention to develop practice that clearly benefits the people with whom you work. Depending on where and how you work, this might include your service users, your team, or students.

5. If selected for audit, you need to send a CPD profile (which must be your own work and supported by evidence) to show how you have met the standards (see Chapter 8). Should this be incomplete, it may be returned to you for further work. If you do not comply with this request, you will usually be removed from the register – unless this is due to 'unavoidable circumstances', in which case you may be allowed to defer (HCPC 2012a, p. 19).

However, it is important to note that these are current HCPC requirements. These could change in the future and it is therefore advisable to refer to the HCPC website (http://www.hcpc-uk.org.uk) for the most up-to-date information.

For other health professionals in the UK, regulatory bodies such as the Nursing and Midwifery Council (NMC) and the General Medical Council (GMC) set out their own standards for CPD.

To further emphasise the importance of CPD for the health and care professions, the Royal College of Nursing (RCN) produced a joint position statement on behalf of allied health professionals and nurses and midwives (2007). In this statement, they recommended that the professions represented should be granted a minimum of 45 hours of protected time dedicated to CPD and stated that CPD is 'fundamental to the development of all health and social care practitioners and is the mechanism through which high quality patient and client care is identified, maintained and developed' (RCN 2007, p. 2).

Regulation has been helpful in raising the significance of CPD for both staff and organisations, encouraging staff to undertake and record it with reference to its impact on service users (HCPC 2012a). However, although this type of audit highlights measurement against standards of CPD, it does not clearly demonstrate impact on practice. The biennial review of standards also means that people can be 'strategic' about their practice and recording of CPD, rather than making it an integral part of their work. There has been much discussion about the question of when routine work practice becomes CPD, and this is discussed in more depth in Chapter 3.

TRAMmCPD (Morris *et al.* 2011, Lawson *et al.* 2014) has been developed as a framework and set of tools to attempt a more thoughtfully strategic and integrated approach to CPD.

International requirements for CPD

Requirements differ from country to country, regarding visas, registration, qualifications to work, language proficiency and CPD. Table 1.2 provides some useful links should you be considering working inside (or outside) the UK as part of your professional development. It may also be useful to contact your own professional body, or that of the country you are planning to work in, for advice.

Table 1.2 International CPD requirements

Country	Useful links
Australia/Canada/Europe/United States/New Zealand/UK	Visa information is available at: *http://www.emigrate2.co.uk* (Accessed 24 April 2015)
Australia	The Australian Health Practitioner Regulation Agency governs the operations of the national boards; each board has its own standards and provides guidance. Information available at: *http://www.ahpra.gov.au/Education/Continuing-Professional-Development.aspx* (Accessed 24 April 2015)
Canada	Health Canada provides information and guidance: *http://www.hc-sc.gc.ca/hcs-sss/hhr-rhs/strateg/init-prof-educ/index-eng.php* (Accessed 24 April 2015) Check with your professional body for CPD or Continuing Professional Education guidance (CPE)
Ireland	Information available at: *http://www.citizensinformation.ie/en/moving_country/moving_to_ireland/working_in_ireland* (Accessed 24 April 2015) CORU is the multi-professional regulator that provides CPD guidelines: *http://www.coru.ie* (Accessed 24 April 2015)
South Africa	The Health Professions Council of South Africa is the regulatory body for 12 professional boards. Information is available at: *http://www.hpcsa.co.za* (Accessed 24 April 2015) Their professional CPD guidance is available at: *http://www.hpcsa.co.za/CPD/ForProfessionals* (Accessed 24 April 2015)
United Kingdom (UK)	Passport and living abroad information: *https://www.gov.uk/browse/abroad* (Accessed 24 April 2015) Visa and immigration information: *https://www.gov.uk/browse/visas-immigration* (Accessed 24 April 2015) The HCPC, the regulatory body for health and care professionals in the UK, can provide information and guidance and set the standards for CPD (HCPC 2012c) *http://www.hcpc-uk.org/apply/international* (Accessed 24 April 2015)

United States of America (USA)	States across America have different mandatory requirements for health professionals, which range from no requirements to a set numbers of hours or units (or a mixture of the two) over a period of time. USA government information about working is available at: *https://www.usa.gov/find-a-job* (Accessed 11 September 2015) The Department of Homeland Security has information about obtaining a permanent resident status available at: *http://www.uscis.gov/greencard* (Accessed 24 April 2015) Check your professional body for more guidance and information regarding CPD requirements in individual US states.

How do you undertake and demonstrate CPD?

In the past, CPD relied on the individual collecting a series of certificates or points to show that a course had been attended and a specified amount of CPD undertaken. Although there are many free courses available, which can be an invaluable way of helping you to develop personally and professionally, such courses are not the only means of undertaking CPD, and Chapter 6 explores this in more detail.

It should also be remembered that simply attending a course or workshop does not in itself constitute CPD. The CPD is what you then do with what you have learnt, and how you evidence this learning. In the next section we introduce you to our case study practitioner, Sally. We will revisit Sally in future chapters, to illustrate how TRAMmCPD might help you maximise your CPD. Although Sally is an occupational therapist, her learning experience applies equally to any of the HCPC-registered professions.

Case study: Introducing Sally

Sally is an occupational therapist registered with the HCPC. She has been working for nine months, having qualified a year ago. She is currently in a Band Five post in community mental health, following six months in orthopaedics. She is due to move into her third rotation on the neurological rehabilitation ward in three months' time.

Sally has just completed her first review as part of her preceptorship programme and knows she now has to undertake some CPD in the forthcoming year. She is aware that there is a conference coming up in two months' time so, having gained permission from her manager, she registers to attend. Attendance is free but her manager has allowed her to take the time off work, and has agreed to give her funding of up to £200 for travel and accommodation.

Sally arrives at the conference and glances at the programme, which looks complicated. She decides to tag along with her friend who is attending a seminar that will last for the first morning. It is in the same building and is next to the coffee room where she is currently, so this seems to be the most sensible option. At lunch she meets a group of friends with whom she went to university and soon realises that she has missed the start of the next set of presentations. She decides to have a wander around the poster display and then onto the exhibition, where she collects lots of information and freebies from the exhibitors' stands. At the next coffee break she hears that there is a session on social media, which she is interested in, so she goes to that.

At the end of the social media session, Sally thinks she has done everything she was supposed to do and therefore ticks off CPD on her appraisal objectives. She has attended a conference, gone to the sessions, seen posters and collected loads of free information. She's not too keen on doing the same tomorrow but she needs to stay in order to get her certificate of attendance. She then heads back to the hotel.

In the hotel Sally unpacks her conference bag. Amongst the free pens and leaflets, she finds the conference programme. She looks at the timetable for the following day and notices a seminar on stroke rehabilitation during the morning, which she thinks would be a good idea to attend. Nothing interests her in the afternoon sessions so she decides to wait and see which sessions her friends are going to.

The following day Sally attends the stroke seminar as planned and finds it really useful. She realises how much more she is enjoying the second day of the conference and wishes she had been more organised the previous day. At lunch, her friends are discussing the afternoon sessions and they all decide to attend the TRAMmCPD workshop, as one of them has been following @TRAMmCPD on Twitter and would like to find out more.

Is this CPD? According to the HCPC, Sally has attended several learning activities, which may have helped her learn some new things, but:

- How could she prepare differently to make the most out of future CPD opportunities?
- How could her manager have encouraged her to prepare more effectively?
- How is Sally going to demonstrate that she has a continuous and up-to-date record of her CPD activities? (See Chapters 3 and 5, HCPC Standard 1.)
- How will she demonstrate that she has undertaken a mixture of learning activities? (See Chapters 3, 6 and 8, HCPC Standard 2.)
- In a year's time, how will Sally remember what she did and what she learnt? (See Chapters 5 and 8, HCPC Standards 1 and 2.)
- How will Sally show that this has contributed to the quality of her practice and service delivery? (See Chapters 5 and 8, HCPC Standards 3 and 4.)
- How will her manager know what she has learnt from attending? (See Chapters 2, 4 and 7, HCPC Standard 3.)
- How will Sally's colleagues benefit from covering for her while she is away? (See Chapter 4, HCPC Standard 3.)
- How will the organisation Sally works for benefit from this? (See Chapters 4 and 8, HCPC Standards 3 and 4.)

This book will explore the ways in which TRAMmCPD can help you address all these issues and meet the HCPC standards for CPD, whatever your particular profession, working situation and experience.

Tasks

The following tasks encourage you to consider what you already know about CPD and what you have done to contribute to this, together with the impact of CPD on your practice:

● If you are an allied health professional, read the HCPC guide *CPD and your registration* (HCPC 2012a) and the HCPC Standards (HCPC 2012c).

● If you are not an HCPC-registered professional, you can still use TRAMmCPD but ensure that you are aware of the requirements of your own regulatory body.

● Have a look on your own professional body website and see what resources they offer to guide and support CPD.

● Read Chapter 2 to discover your preferred learning style/s.

2

Engaging in CPD and developing your learning style

There is no such thing as 'one size fits all' in continuing professional development. This is acknowledged by gatekeepers of CPD such as the HCPC (2012a), which emphasises the value of accessing a variety of activities to strengthen your portfolio. Chapter 6 explores the range and value of some of these activities to help you find the most appropriate form of CPD to suit your requirements. However, there are other critical factors when planning and selecting activities for your CPD pathway.

The first part of this chapter will explore the concept of CPD engagement and the reasons why identifying your preferred learning style is important. It will provide examples of tools to help you identify your own learning style, and then highlight ways to maximise learning according to each style and context. The second part will focus on how to apply these learning skills and explore methods of facilitating their application in practice.

Tasks at the end of the chapter will enable you to explore and revise your most effective learning styles, and you will be given references and links for tools to help you do this.

Engaging in CPD

Much of the literature pertaining to CPD, including the regulations for AHPs (HCPC 2012a), highlight the necessity for individuals to be 'engaged' in CPD. However, in many instances the meaning of the term 'engagement' is unclear. A concept analysis (Hearle 2015, unpublished), conducted in preparation for a research project into the effectiveness of the TRAMm model, identified the following defining attributes of CPD engagement:

● CPD is self-initiated and undertaken voluntarily, rather than as a result of a mandatory requirement.

● The individual feels rewarded either intrinsically (e.g. enjoyment) or extrinsically (e.g. promotion) during or after undertaking CPD.

- The knowledge/skills gained via the CPD are embraced and applied in practice for the benefit of the service/service user.
- Learning is recorded, evaluated, shared with others and is evidenced to continue beyond the initial CPD activity.

In order to fully engage in CPD, the ability to self-direct is crucial. McClelland (1985) discussed the importance of measuring motivation and achievement in order to identify the level of self-directedness of an individual using the Need for Achievement (nAch) Test. Putting nAch into context, it is useful to consider the work of Penman (2014), an occupational therapist, who explored factors influencing approaches to CPD in the research for her doctorate. Penman discovered that in order for individuals to engage, they must show 'readiness' to be self-directed learners. This involves taking responsibility for your own learning and being aware of your own learning needs. To do this, you need to identify your own personal learning style.

What do we mean by individual learning styles?

If we compare ourselves with colleagues, friends or family, it becomes clear that we all have very specific approaches towards activities (whether work or leisure) and the types of roles we perform. For example, some people will be motivated by sporting and team activities or competitions; others will enjoy more individual, quiet activities such as reading or baking. The same applies to learning.

Why does recognising your learning style help your CPD?

Most people are born with the capacity to learn new things. During our lives, and throughout our education, most of us find some things more interesting or easier to learn than others. For instance, some people easily pick up the words to songs, whereas others do not 'hear' the words but easily recognise the tune. Some can read a set of instructions and instinctively know how to assemble a piece of furniture, while others have to look at the diagrams or may even be able to assemble the item just by looking at the parts and the final picture. Our choice of preferred learning style doesn't make one person any 'brighter' than another, and there is no style that suits all. The trick is to recognise the learning style that works best for you.

When identifying your learning style, another consideration is the learning context. This can also be a personal preference. For example, some people learn best through hands-on practice and may therefore find role-play situations or work-based learning most appropriate. Others may learn and be able to apply information just from attending a seminar or lecture and find role-play stressful and unhelpful. Context is also important when considering the learning required. If someone needs to acquire new information about a condition, for example, attending a lecture, conference or reading a book or article may be sufficient. However, if the CPD is aimed at learning a new skill or applying a new intervention, the learning may have to take place in a simulated or work-based setting, regardless of preferred learning style.

The next section examines some of the tools that are available to help you recognise your learning style and preferences and how you can make the best use of this information.

How can you identify your learning style or preference?

One simple and free way to ascertain your preferred learning style is to undertake a written reflection. Following a specific model (see Chapter 5), you should reflect upon a recent activity where you felt you learnt something. Consider which factors you enjoyed and found helpful in terms of learning, and which you found less effective. Also, try to analyse why some factors helped you to learn, and why others did not.

Mind mapping (see Chapter 5) is another way to carry out this exercise. Or you could just create a mind map in order to organise your thoughts for a more detailed reflection.

If you would prefer a more structured method, there are various standardised tools available that will enable you to ascertain your preferred learning style. Some of the most common include:

● VARK (Visual–Auditory–Read/Write–Kinaesthetic) test

● Honey and Mumford Learning Styles Questionnaire

● Kolb's Learning Styles Inventory

● nAch (Need for Achievement)

The VARK test

The VARK test (Fleming & Mills 1992) can be accessed via:

http://vark-learn.com/the-vark-questionnaire

This test consists of a series of 16 questions that explore learning style preferences in given situations. Each question has four possible answers and you are required to select the answer that describes how you would be most likely to behave. Here is an example of the type of question you might find in the VARK test:

You have finished a competition or test and would like some feedback…
a. Using a written description of your results
b. Using a graph showing what you have achieved
c. From somebody who talks it through with you
d. Using examples from what you have done.

At the end of the test, you simply count up the numbers of As, Bs, Cs and Ds to find your preferred style of learning, as follows:

● Visual learners (learn best from visual cues and pictures)

● Auditory learners (learn best from auditory cues, lectures and talking things through)

- Read/write learners (learn best from making lists and notes, and being given handouts)
- Kinaesthetic/tactile learners (learn best from doing things and carrying out activities).

Once you have matched your score to your learning preference, there are explanations of those things that each type of learner finds useful. Some people may be very biased towards one particular style, while others may be quite close in two or more categories. The VARK team stress that, although your score may indicate one preference, this only refers to your learning, which may be influenced by strategies you have developed during your life. It does not suggest how you undertake other things (such as work) or how you behave in relation to other people.

The test is free and you can access other learning support media through the website.

The Kolb Learning Style Inventory and Honey and Mumford Learning Styles

Kolb suggests that there are four main stages in learning:

1. **Concrete experience**, in which the individual encounters a new experience or situation or reinterprets an existing experience
2. **Reflective observation**, in which the individual reflects on the experience, noting differences between the experience and their understanding
3. **Abstract conceptualisation**, in which the reflection stimulates a new idea or modification
4. **Active experimentation**, in which learning is applied and evaluated.

In Kolb's cycle, no one stage is more important than any other so the learner can enter the cycle at any point. However, he argues that the most effective learning occurs when the individual moves through all four stages.

As in the VARK test, Kolb believes that individuals tend to prefer one learning style above another. This preference is influenced by various factors, including the person's social environment, their educational experiences and their own cognitive makeup. However, he also emphasises that this does not provide an excuse to make sole use of that preferred style. Instead individuals must work on those areas where learning is less comfortable in order to gain a more rounded and effective learning experience. To help you explore different types of learning, Kolb offers a specific Learning Style Inventory, which is available at:

http://learningfromexperience.com/tools/kolb-learning-style-inventory-lsi/

There is also the Honey and Mumford (1992) Learning Styles Questionnaire, based on Kolb, which is available at:

http://www.peterhoney.com/

Reflecting the principles of Kolb's learning cycle, Honey and Mumford give you the choice of completing one of two questionnaires – one of 40 or one of 80 statements. Whichever one you choose, you are asked to answer as honestly as possible by agreeing or disagreeing with each statement. Once you have completed the questionnaire, you can transfer your responses to a grid, which will give you a score out of 20 for each of the following learning style categories:

1. **The Activist**: you learn by doing, or by having an experience

2. **The Reflector**: you learn by reviewing the experience from a number of perspectives

3. **The Theorist**: you need to understand the underpinning theories, drawing conclusions from the experience

4. **The Pragmatist**: you learn by seeing how to put into practice, and planning the next steps.

Once you have highlighted your preferred style/s, and those which are more problematic for you, Honey and Mumford provide descriptors and action plans for each one.

Maintaining a self-directed approach

Having identified your preferred learning style and selected an area you wish to know more about in order to improve your work with service users, how do you bring all this together in order to apply your learning in practice?

It's clearly important to be aware of your learning preferences and apply them, but these are not the only factors involved in engagement in CPD. A number of external factors are considered later (in Chapter 3), but one core element of being a professional is the internal factor of maintaining a desire to know more (Bargagliotti 2012). This is supported by Penman (2014) with her idea of the link between readiness for self-directed learning and CPD engagement. Penman (2014, p. 1) states that this readiness is influenced by 'beliefs or attitudes to learning, the degree of metacognitive awareness [of themselves] as learners, and personal definitions of competence to practice, with experience in supervision of allied health students and occupational therapists, and years employed'.

This idea of self-directedness relates to all aspects of the CPD process, which we will discuss broadly in Chapter 3 and in greater depth in Chapters 4 to 8. The first step is to identify your own learning development plan; and the best way to do this is to consider and document your aspirational career pathway or immediate goals for professional development. These can be most effectively articulated by generating Specific, Measurable, Achievable, Realistic and Timely (SMART) objectives (see example below).

Your SMART objectives should be negotiated and agreed with your supervisor or as part of your regular appraisal. You may also wish to discuss your plans with your mentor prior to this (see Chapters 7 and 8). You can either do this by writing a set of objectives or use a more structured tool such as a learning contract (see Chapter 5). Remember, whatever you decide, you must write the objectives as something you want to achieve rather than something you are going to do.

For example:

'To spend time with the community rehabilitation team by the end of the month'

is a passive activity that may not result in any learning.

It would be better to reword it as:

'Through a written reflection, I will demonstrate a comprehensive understanding of the role and scope of the community rehabilitation team and compare it with my role in social care. This is to be achieved within the next four weeks and validated by my line manager.'

This objective requires active participation, leading to a measurable outcome. To make it more detailed, you could indicate the evidence you will provide to show you have gained the comprehensive understanding.

Applying your learning in practice

For allied health professionals, the main purpose of CPD is undoubtedly to foster improvement in care for service users (HCPC 2012a, RCN 2007). The fourth HCPC Standard requires you to provide evidence to demonstrate how you have achieved this through CPD (HCPC 2012c). The various ways to measure the success of your CPD will be explored in depth in Chapter 8 but it is important to begin by considering how to apply this learning in practice.

Delors (1996, p. 92) identified four pillars of lifelong learning and education, highlighting those aspects that people need to consider when undertaking CPD (rather than simply focusing on the acquisition of new knowledge). These four pillars will guide you in how to apply your learning in practice:

1. 'Learning to know', which means mastering learning tools. You could ask yourself 'How have I developed in the way that I have, and what has helped me?' or 'What learning tools do I have at my disposal?'

2. 'Learning to do', which means gaining the skills needed for the current and future workplace. You could ask yourself 'What new skills have I learnt and how will they help me improve the care of my patients/service users? Where is my evidence for this?'

3. 'Learning to live together and with others', which involves, for example, conflict resolution and respecting the influence of other cultures. Here, you might ask yourself 'What knowledge and skills have I developed that will help me to work with or manage others, or work in complex situations? How can I demonstrate that I have put these into practice?'

4. 'Learning to be', which means education that contributes to a person's complete development. This might include your professional or other higher education qualifications, which address more than just knowledge and skills. In these circumstances, growth is often both personal and professional so you may ask yourself 'How have I changed the way I practise as a professional? What elements of my practice demonstrate my growth in confidence?'

Although maintenance and/or improvement of practice quality is usually the main stated reason for undertaking CPD (HCPC 2012a), CPD activity often fails to translate into better practice. It is widely accepted that many healthcare professionals do not make sufficient use of evidence-based research, and this has led to inefficiency and ineffectiveness in delivering services (Davis *et al.*

2003, Straus *et al.* 2009, Legare *et al.* 2011). Despite this, the government and many professional healthcare bodies appear to be in little doubt that undertaking CPD leads to an improvement in patient outcomes. It is therefore useful to consider ways in which our learning from CPD can actually be applied to benefit our service users.

One concept that appears to assist this understanding is 'knowledge translation'. This is a Canadian term that describes bridging the gap between theory and practice (Straus *et al.* 2009). Other terms used to describe this include 'research use', 'knowledge transfer and exchange' (in the USA) and 'implementation science and research utilisation' (in the UK and Europe).

According to the Canadian Institutes of Health Research (CIHR) (2005), knowledge translation involves all the CPD steps from the creation of new knowledge to its application to ensure benefits for society. Authors writing on this subject consider that knowledge translation provides a holistic framework in healthcare, encompassing both continuing education and CPD, and focusing on using high-quality evidence to change health outcomes (Davis *et al.* 2003, Legare 2011).

Knowledge translation has many definitions but usually includes the following criteria:

1. It occurs in the practice or clinical setting, rather than a classroom or other simulated learning environment.

2. It has an explicit (and justified) need for change in health outcome or behaviour, involving the agreement of all potential stakeholders.

3. It involves a process of knowledge creation, inquiry, synthesis and creation of tools, reflecting the needs of all potential stakeholders, including service users and carers.

4. It includes a toolkit, guideline, checklist or pathway that has synthesised and translated recent, high-quality and reliable evidence into unambiguous techniques for practical application.

5. It has a clear process for evaluating knowledge application and for ensuring continued activity.

Following these criteria should ensure appropriate application of the knowledge and skills you acquire through CPD.

To further support this concept of knowledge translation, Cusick and McCluskey (2000) stress the importance of applying evidence-based practice learnt from CPD to improve clinical effectiveness. In order to do this, they recommend a range of strategies, including:

● Changing practitioners' or stakeholders' (such as service users' or managers') behaviour and/or expectations

● Using theory to inform the effective integration of into practice (such as knowledge translation)

● Developing organisational requirements for the application of evidence-based practice

● Supporting professional association initiatives and the development of clinical guidelines.

Cusick and McCluskey (2000) propose that practitioners need to be aware of the above strategies before developing their own CPD development plan.

Case study: Sally investigates her learning style

In the first chapter we introduced Sally, an occupational therapist who was funded by her employer to attend a two-day conference, where she went to several ad hoc sessions with no forethought or planning. At the end of the second day, she participated in a TRAMmCPD workshop, where she was introduced to the model and its tools. At this point, she realised there was more to CPD than she originally thought and decided that she needed to become more strategic in her approach to her CPD in order to make the most of her career.

In her drive to be more strategic, Sally realises she needs to become more proactive with her CPD and decides to explore her preferred learning style, as suggested in the TRAMmCPD workshop she attended. Sally decides to carry out some self-directed informal research on the Internet, where she finds a range of resources that may help her identify her learning style. She is particularly drawn to the resources available on the VARK website (Fleming & Mills 1992) and she would also like to try Honey and Mumford (1992) because she knows their questionnaire is based on Kolb's Learning Cycle, a learning framework with which she is already familiar.

Following completion of the VARK test, Sally realises she is primarily a kinaesthetic learner, with visual tendencies. She then undertakes the Honey and Mumford Learning Styles Questionnaire, which reveals that she is predominantly an Activist and notes that her Reflector category is very low and this is an area she needs to work on.

Now that she is aware of her preferred learning style, Sally understands that she learns best by 'doing' and this will need to be her focus, where possible, when planning the best ways to learn new skills. The tests suggest that she will learn best by attending interactive workshops, shadowing and work-based learning, rather than attending lectures or presentations. Whichever CPD activity she chooses, she now knows that she must find ways to participate actively, as sitting listening in lectures and presentations does not stimulate her ability to learn.

As an Activist (based on the Honey and Mumford questionnaire), she realises she needs assistance to increase such opportunities for practical learning and participation. This does not mean that Sally should only consider practical activities for her CPD, as this may not always be possible or practicable. For example, if Sally attends a lecture she may need to consider strategies such as making notes that involve practical application to real-life people she is working with, or has worked with, rather than simply recording the main points from the lecture.

The results from the Honey and Mumford questionnaire remind Sally that reflective skills are not her strength so she needs to seek ways to encourage and challenge her skills of reflection. Previously, she has used Gibbs' reflective cycle (1988), which she remembers was easy to use and understand.

All her preferred learning style information can be used when considering her future learning needs, and this will provide a good focus for her CPD over the next few months. Happy with the progress she has made, she decides to discuss her plans at her next supervision.

This chapter has highlighted the conditions required for CPD engagement, discussed the need to apply the knowledge and skills gained, and suggested ways in which this might be achieved. It has also discussed the importance of understanding your preferred learning style, and explored a few tools and strategies to help you identify your preferences.

Tasks

The following tasks will enable you to explore, revise and consolidate your most effective learning styles and help you use this information to engage more effectively with CPD:

- Have a look at the suggested learning styles websites to see if any of the tests or questionnaires are useful to you. If not, investigate further examples.

- Complete one of the preferred learning style tests or questionnaires to see what they suggest about you. Do you agree?

- What are your learning needs, in addition to your preferred learning styles identified above?

- Arrange a meeting with your supervisor or mentor to explore what actions you can take as a result of the above findings.

- Consider what you could do to foster a conducive CPD environment within your work environment. Discuss your ideas with your manager if this is something you are not able to implement yourself.

- If you are a manager reading this chapter, consider how you might alter your management or teaching style to reflect individual learning needs within each of the categories of Kolb and Honey and Mumford.

- Reflect on your most recent CPD activity. Have you applied the information you learnt? If so, how? If not, what could you have done to make this CPD valuable?

- Read Chapter 3 to learn more about CPD, and the TRAMm model and its tools and how they can help you.

3

Introduction to the TRAMm model

This chapter introduces mechanisms for strategic CPD using TRAMmCPD. It explains why the TRAMm model and its associated tools were developed and how they can help you plan and execute appropriate professional development to meet your own needs as well as those of your service users and the organisation in which you work. It outlines the main components (stations) of the model and explores how the model and its tools can be used, illustrating its application with a case study and real working examples.

Tasks at the end of the chapter encourage you to identify core learning needs in relation to your personal and professional development using TRAMmCPD. You can also consider how you might use TRAMmCPD to provide a framework for your professional development.

Why do we need a model for CPD?

The CPD Audit Report (HCPC 2014b) highlights evidence suggesting that those who undertake CPD are less likely to find themselves the subject of a complaint or concern and are more likely to be, or become, reflective practitioners. The TRAMm model was designed after initial investigations to explore potential structures for professional development support groups revealed a scarcity of frameworks to clarify the purpose and guide the process of CPD.

The importance of CPD engagement

In Chapter 2 we saw that it is part of our professional responsibility to undertake CPD; but undertaking CPD is not enough in itself. Certain factors also need to be in place to enable us to engage with CPD. What do we mean by the concept of engagement in relation to CPD?

Much has been written on the subject of worker/employee engagement in CPD; yet the meaning of CPD engagement remains less than clear. In order to develop the TRAMm model, a concept analysis was undertaken and the following criteria emerged:

I. When an individual is engaged, the CPD activity is *self-initiated* and undertaken *voluntarily*, rather than purely because it is a mandatory requirement.

2. The motivation to undertake the activity can be intrinsic or extrinsic. The individual feels *rewarded* either intrinsically (e.g. through their own enjoyment), or extrinsically (e.g. through promotion), while undertaking or after undertaking the CPD activity.

3. The knowledge and skills gained via the CPD are embraced and *applied* in practice for the benefit of the organisation and service user/s.

4. Learning is *recorded, evaluated and shared* with others.

5. Learning is shown to *continue beyond* the initial CPD activity.

Although the TRAMm model was initially designed as a CPD guide for individuals, to give them the best opportunity to engage with their own professional development, the organisation in which they work must also accept some responsibility for supporting its employees.

Simpson (2009) identified the availability of resources as an especially important factor in encouraging employee engagement, especially as CPD is usually undertaken in the workplace. However, despite the continuing emphasis on the importance of CPD in practice, anecdotal evidence from managers and practitioners suggests that the resources (including money and time) available for CPD in organisations appear to have been reduced in recent years. Not surprisingly, this has subsequently appeared to result in a lack of engagement in CPD (AMRC 2010, Gould et al. 2007).

The rise in employee workload, and the individual guilt associated with taking time away from critical patient care, are other factors thought to result in disengagement from CPD (O'Sullivan 2003, 2006). In contrast, those employers considered to be 'learning organisations' (O'Sullivan 2006) encourage their employees to engage with their own CPD by supporting them and offering them opportunities to identify and address their learning and development needs. In learning organisations, evidence-based practice is encouraged and processes such as appraisal, supervision, mentorship and preceptorship (see Chapters 7 and 8) help to create and maintain a supportive environment. If individuals are encouraged in this way, they are likely to be more engaged with their work, which in turn stimulates a drive to learn more in order to keep improving the quality of their work. CPD engagement thus becomes a virtuous cycle. Having said this, it is important to acknowledge that the opposite may sometimes occur – when burnout in an existing role can lead to an extrinsic desire for CPD to facilitate a change in career direction.

We are *not* saying that a lack of time and money means that you cannot be expected to engage in CPD; but we *are* acknowledging a mutual responsibility, as CPD clearly offers shared benefits for both the individual and organisation. Subsequent chapters will explore ways in which you and your organisation can work together in this way.

Effective CPD, where individuals are fully engaged with their own professional development, has been found to correlate with a higher quality of care for the service user (DH 2001, AHPP 2003, AMRC 2010, HCPC 2015a). Service users are bound to benefit when CPD is undertaken by individual staff members motivated by a need to know more and to find evidence supporting the effectiveness (or otherwise) of different types of patient intervention.

It is also widely accepted that work engagement leads to greater job satisfaction and therefore less chance of burnout (Maslach 2001, Van der Broeck et al. 2008, Schaufeli & Bakker 2004). If a person is engaged in their work, they have a drive to know more and to strive for best practice, which is furthered by their engagement in CPD. Hence, it also likely that CPD engagement will result in greater learner satisfaction and job satisfaction and subsequently in higher retention of staff (O'Sullivan 2006, AMRC 2010).

A further consequence of full engagement in CPD is the wider dissemination of learning (AMRC 2010, Chapter 2) and hence the potential for the learning to benefit more service users. The potential benefits apply to service users treated by the individual and their immediate colleagues and also to those treated by a much wider range of professionals within organisations, by means of publication in peer-reviewed journals and presentations at national or international conferences.

Different approaches to CPD

It is not possible to design a CPD programme to fit every single person, as we all have different approaches to our learning and skills development. However, a model or framework can help to draw the necessary components of CPD together into a cohesive whole, providing a structure for this complex and often misunderstood process, while respecting the unique requirements of each individual.

Before exploring how the TRAMm model can assist you in planning and organising your CPD in a more strategic and efficient way, it may be helpful for you to examine the approach you usually take to the process of CPD.

Consider the following examples, which portray a range of approaches to CPD. As you read them, think about which one most closely matches your own style. You may find that more than one applies to you, but be honest about which one fits you best.

Example 3.1 The ostrich

George is a social worker, who has been qualified for 22 years. He works in an English town at the local hospital, as part of the older adult team. He is conscious that social workers have now joined the HCPC and he will be required to change his CPD practice in line with the new guidelines. He is aware that social workers will be called for audit in the next two years but is fairly certain he won't be one of the 'unlucky' ones. He therefore plans to keep his head down and worry about it if and when it happens.

Example 3.2 The procrastinator

Sarina is a Band 7 podiatrist, who works as part of the same older adult team as George. She knows that each time the podiatry audit comes around it could well apply to her. She has dutifully undertaken her CPD during each of the six years she has been qualified, usually attending courses following recommendations from her manager. She is aware that she hasn't started to make records in her portfolio, but often thinks about how to do it and plans to make a start 'next week'. Sadly, next week just never seems to arrive.

Example 3.3 The bull in a china shop

Ben, a physiotherapist, has been qualified for nearly two years. He is very enthusiastic about his work and is always very busy in his role in the outpatients department of an inner-city hospital. He is keen to ensure that he stays as up to date as possible and is very conscientious about CPD. He is proud of the fact that he has already been on 13 short courses and conferences on a wide variety of topics (some in his own time) and has just lined up two more one-day refresher sessions over the next three months. He has two A4 lever-arch folders full of reflections, course notes and certificates. Although these files are not yet organised, he has a lot to show people if they ask to see his CPD records.

Example 3.4 The strategist

Janet has recently obtained a Band 5 speech and language therapist post and is currently awaiting her final results before she can apply for her HCPC registration. Previously a healthcare assistant with no formal qualifications, Janet was keen to continue to work in a healthcare setting but in a more defined and professional role. After deciding that speech and language therapy was her chosen career path, she successfully completed the appropriate A-levels at evening classes, which enabled her to qualify for university. While awaiting the results of her final exams, she is continuing to plan her professional development. Having attended a TRAMmCPD workshop, she has consolidated her strategic skills at university, based on the HCPC standards, using TRAMmCPD. She is hoping to work with children and is currently focusing her CPD on this area, through volunteering at a local specialist school. This will mean that she is well placed to apply for relevant posts as they arise.

Which example resembles you most closely? Clearly, most of us would aspire to emulate Janet ('the strategist'). She is focused on her career path and takes a strategic approach to reaching her objectives. However, if you find yourself more closely resembling one of the others, you are by no means on your own – and this can be easily rectified.

For instance, if you are most like George ('the ostrich'), you really need to take your head out of the sand and start to embrace CPD. Begin by getting a portfolio together, using the items you have already gathered. You should also think about those activities you have undertaken in the last 12 months that could be classed as CPD (see Chapter 6). Carry out a couple of reflections to evidence your learning and make an appointment with your line manager or supervisor to discuss some objectives to take you through to the next appraisal.

If you find you resemble Sarina ('the procrastinator'), get a file or find an electronic portfolio structure. Then undertake a couple of reflections or look at evidencing the outcomes of this CPD via a case study. Think carefully about where you see your future direction and talk to your supervisor about the strategic direction of the organisation so that you can help initiate your own plans for any future CPD, rather than waiting to be told by your manager.

If you are like Ben ('the bull'), your enthusiasm is to be commended but you really need to start refining what you do and focus on quality rather than quantity. Set aside a couple of half-days to go through all your reflections and certificates and get them organised into a portfolio. You could perhaps undertake one reflection on your CPD as a whole, to date. Then see if there are any themes arising from the CPD you have already done, and which CPD activities you think have been most useful. This should give you an idea of your future direction, and which aspects of CPD you should pursue in future.

Once you have a clear awareness of your current approach and have got to grips with what you have achieved to date, you need to consider how TRAMmCPD can provide a framework to help you understand ways to address your future development and learning needs.

What is TRAMm?

The TRAMm model has been developed as a dynamic, interactive model to facilitate a strategic approach to CPD (Morris *et al.* 2011, Lawson 2014). CPD is now mandatory for allied health professionals, and this model uses an outcomes-based approach, whereby the aims of CPD are based on its impact, rather than the simple 'doing' of CPD. Although there have been many different approaches to CPD, research revealed that none of them brought together all the HCPC's requirements into a coherent whole. The TRAMm model was therefore initially designed to assist professionals registered with the HCPC to engage in and evidence CPD as part of their biennial registration process. However, the principles of this model are equally applicable for any individual who needs to continue their professional development (such as nurses, doctors, lawyers and many other professionals).

The TRAMm model is based on the fact that professionals not only need to learn new information and skills but they also need to plan their professional development, apply their newly acquired knowledge and skills within practice, measure their success (or otherwise), and share evidence of their practice with others. New knowledge not only adds value; it also provides the ability to deliver high-quality care. When knowledge is transferred into practice, it deepens the individual's ability to create, share, disseminate and present.

Continuing professional development is an individual journey that reflects the core unique qualities and skills of each practitioner. To be successful, it should be a strategic journey that is planned according to the individual's needs in relation to their professional practice and the organisation in which they work. It should contain a mixture of activities that reflect the preferred learning styles of the individual (see Chapter 2) and the type of knowledge or skill required in their practice. For example, there would be little point in simply reading a textbook if the main aim of the CPD was to develop your neurological handling skills. The textbook might help you acquire knowledge but could not replace actual practice for developing the skill itself. Undertaking activities alone does not constitute CPD. Instead, it is important on this journey that the individual applies what they have learnt from the activity/ies in practice, and monitors their progress and success, before measuring the final outcome and readjusting their practice accordingly.

The TRAMm model has been designed alongside tools (the TRAMm Tracker and TRAMm Trail) for recording your CPD. Together, the model and tools are known as TRAMmCPD. TRAMmCPD can be used by individuals and also by the organisations in which they work. While individuals are more likely to use this to plan and record their CPD, organisations may choose to adopt TRAMmCPD as a corporate tool by which CPD is facilitated and measured. This is illustrated by the following example.

Example 3.5 The potential use of TRAMmCPD

Allyson is a physiotherapist who has recently read about TRAMmCPD in her colleague's professional body newsletter (Lawson *et al.* 2014). She has accessed the website and downloaded the free TRAMmCPD tools and the information about how to apply them. She has opened an electronic portfolio, following the TRAMmCPD stations, and has started using the tools to record the details of her CPD. After taking this to a supervision session with her therapy lead, she has been asked to present TRAMm to the team – so that all therapy professionals across the health board can adopt this as a framework to structure, present and measure their CPD.

What are the TRAMm stations?

In order to reflect the full CPD journey, TRAMm is divided into five core stations: 'Tell', 'Record', 'Activity', 'Monitor' and 'measure'. You will note that measure is denoted by a lower case 'm'. This is solely to differentiate it from 'Monitor' and in no way reflects the relative importance afforded to each station.

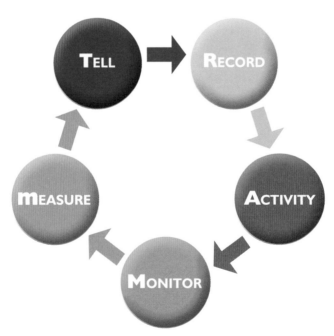

Figure 3.1 The TRAMm stations

Each of the five TRAMm stations is briefly summarised below. (They are explained in detail in Chapters 4–8.)

Station T (Tell, see Chapter 4): 'Tell' is about articulating and planning what you need or would like to learn (professional development planning) and disseminating information about what you have learnt.

Station R (Record, see Chapter 5): 'Record' refers to the systematic documentation of what you have learnt, how you have put it into practice and your reflections on the process, including what you need to learn next. It may also include the recording of outcomes and practice critique.

Station A (Activity, see Chapter 6): 'Activities' are the things you do in order to learn something or develop new knowledge or skills.

Station M (Monitor, see Chapter 7): 'Monitor' refers to keeping track of your development or reviewing your progress so you can alter your approach or change direction if you find that what you are doing is not meeting your learning needs.

Station m (measure, see Chapter 8): 'measure' means keeping track of your progress through tangible outcomes, such as achievement of goals, audit targets and success factors. Measurement does not need to be complex but does require validation in order to provide evidence of achievement.

Table 3.1 provides examples of possible activities within each of the stations. These lists are by no means exhaustive and you may well be able to add to them.

Table 3.1 Examples of entries for each of the TRAMm stations

T – TELL (Chapter 4)	R – RECORD (Chapter 5)
● Informal and formal discussions with colleagues/Meetings	● Reflective logs
● Annual appraisals	● Mind maps
● Planning in supervision	● Learning contracts
● Conferences/Courses/Presentations	● Professional Development Portfolios
● Workshops/Team-building exercises	● Curriculum Vitae
● Training/Roadshows/Away days	● TRAMm Tracker
● Sharing case studies/Storytelling	● TRAMm Trail
● Providing feedback from CPD	
● Social media/Email/Intranet/Internet	
● Writing for publication	
● Pilot/Projects/Evaluation reports	

A – ACTIVITY (Chapter 6)	
● Liaising with other professionals and agencies	● Formal educational study
● Work-based learning	● Taking students
● Shadowing/Secondments/Rotation	● Joining a professional body or specialist section/Becoming an interest group member
● Journal clubs	● External examining
● In-service training	● Preceptorship/Supervision/Mentor-ship/ Coaching
● Mentoring/Teaching courses	
● Professional and external activities	● Informal peer group support
● Courses/Conferences/Workshops	● Discussion with colleagues
● Accreditation/Approval/Revalidation	● Learning from others
● Further and Higher Education	● E-learning/Social Media
● Research	● Self-directed learning
● Project Work	● Informal research
● Reading journals and books	● Verbal or written reflection

M – MONITOR (Chapter 7)	m – measure (Chapter 8)
● Supervision	● Appraisal/Specific individualised goals
● Mentorship	● Reflection/Skill acquisition and improvement
● Preceptorship or equivalent	● Using outcome measures/Performance indicators/Audit/Regulation/Standards of proficiency
● Peer review	
● Self-monitoring through reflection	
	● Peer review
	● Preceptorship
	● Undertaking research/Quality improvement projects
	● Measuring cost effectiveness
	● Miscellaneous (e.g. letters of commendation and awards)

How does the TRAMm model work?

The TRAMm model allows you to identify the gaps in your CPD, by reviewing each station and identifying those you still need to visit in order to maximise your engagement in CPD and its impact for yourself and all the stakeholders involved. Identifying gaps in your experience and knowledge for evidence-based practice (EBP) enables you to seek and plan activities for your CPD. The TRAMm model's flexible approach allows you to visit each station as and when appropriate. This is why it is depicted as a circle, rather than a linear series of stages. Although CPD usually starts with an activity, this is not always the case. For example, a discussion with a colleague or manager may trigger an idea that requires further exploration or training so that it can be effectively applied in practice.

As part of the model, two tools have been designed to assist you in recording and monitoring your CPD: the TRAMm Tracker, in which you can record your CPD journey; and the TRAMm Trail, which enables you to plan and analyse specific aspects of your CPD in greater detail. Collectively, the TRAMm model, TRAMm Tracker and TRAMm Trail are known as TRAMmCPD (see Chapter 5 for full details of these tools). TRAMmCPD has been piloted over 12 months, during which it was further refined to reflect constructive feedback from those who took part in the evaluation.

Why do you need TRAMmCPD?

There are three core reasons why TRAMmCPD can be a useful resource:

1. It can help individuals maximise their professional potential
2. It can enable individuals to meet the HCPC standards for CPD
3. It can contribute to the creation of a learning organisation.

Maximising the individual's professional potential

TRAMmCPD can help you become (more) strategic and maximise your career potential. CPD can be a complex lifelong journey, which requires you to plan your career progression strategically, while at the same time meeting the needs of the organisation within which you work. TRAMmCPD encourages you to plot your journey, record your progress and monitor outcomes, while ensuring that you achieve a balance between your own needs and those of the service users you work with.

Meeting the HCPC's standards for CPD

TRAMmCPD can also help you meet the HCPC standards for CPD (HCPC 2012c). In the United Kingdom, most health and care professionals have to be registered with their statutory body. For allied health professionals (AHPs), the HCPC is commissioned by the government to regulate fitness to practise and they provide standards of proficiency for each regulated profession. The aim is to ensure that all registrants practice lawfully, safely, skilfully and effectively. The HCPC also has a remit to ensure that all registrants undertake CPD, which must adhere to five specific standards (see Chapter 1). These CPD standards form part of a biennial audit process whereby registrants are required to demonstrate their ability to meet these standards and maintain ethical practice. Using the TRAMm model, TRAMm Tracker and TRAMm Trail (TRAMmCPD) gives you a framework to facilitate your engagement in CPD and provide evidence of this process.

Contributing to the creation of a learning organisation

Although initially designed for individuals, TRAMmCPD can also be a useful resource for organisations and their managers because it offers a way of structuring CPD within the workplace and contributing to the establishment of a learning organisation (p. 22). Within the pilot evaluation, some departments adopted TRAMmCPD to provide a consistent approach to CPD across the team, using the tools to monitor progress and facilitate discussion in supervision or appraisal sessions.

During the pilot evaluation of TRAMmCPD, and following examination of HCPC documentation including their CPD standards (HCPC 2012c), a frequently asked question has been 'How do I know when my routine work activity has developed into CPD?' There is no definitive answer, but considering the following questions may help you answer it:

- Have you reached a point at which you are no longer working on automatic pilot?
- Are you employing an activity (see Chapter 6) in order to learn something new?
- Has your usual intervention had an unintended consequence? Have you reflected on the reasons for this and will you change your practice as a result?
- Have you been asked to undertake something new, of which you have little or no experience?
- Through supervision or appraisal, have you identified a new way of working or are you beginning to develop advanced skills in order to further your career?
- Having attended a training event in the past, have you recently used the knowledge gained to improve a service user's outcome?
- Does mapping your usual work activity into TRAMmCPD show that you are in fact developing your practice and it has developed into CPD?

If the answer to any of these questions is 'yes', then it seems that your normal work practice has indeed moved across into the path of CPD and can therefore be documented as such.

How can you use the TRAMm model?

Although TRAMm is represented as a circular model, it is designed to be used as a dynamic framework, in which all stations are linked and can interact to provide a strategic approach to CPD. The stations can be visited in any order, and be visited more than once, while some stations may not be visited at all in relation to a single part of your CPD.

Although not every part of your CPD will visit every TRAMm station, within your total professional journey you should aim to include each of the five elements of TRAMm at regular intervals. The TRAMm Tracker can be used to help you identify those stations not yet addressed or those you are avoiding, and this will help you monitor your CPD progress.

Example 3.6 Using the TRAMm Tracker

Mark is a radiographer. Six months ago, he attended a conference where he attended a seminar discussing a new way of undertaking a technique that had been piloted in three local hospitals. Following the conference, Mark completed his TRAMm Tracker, indicating only that he had undertaken an activity. Six months on, he believes that several new service users could benefit from this new practice. He reads further about it, then approaches his team manager, who asks him to plan a strategy for its implementation (including criteria for use). Mark is aware that he has few entries under 'measurement' on the Tracker so they discuss ways of rectifying this during supervision.

Case study: Sally revisits TRAMmCPD

In Chapter 1 we introduced Sally, an occupational therapist who was funded by her employer to attend a two-day conference. At the end of the second day she participated in a TRAMmCPD workshop, where she was introduced to the HCPC standards for CPD and the TRAMm model and its tools. In Chapter 2, Sally explored her learning styles and realised that she needed to be proactive, rather than just sitting listening to lectures and attending workshops. She needed to make notes, ask questions and apply the information. She also needed to develop her reflective skills.

After using the TRAMmCPD tools in the conference workshop, Sally has decided to use TRAMmCPD to plan and structure her CPD and portfolio. She decides to read the information about the TRAMm model that she was given at the conference. She wants to refresh her memory, as she is aware that she did not fully absorb all the information during the workshop. From her learning styles preferences (explored in Chapter 2), she knows that she has to do more than just read the information in order to understand it thoroughly. She thinks about the conference she recently attended and links what she did there to the five stations of the TRAMm model. She decides she has visited every TRAMm station, with the following justification:

- **T** (Tell) – yes, she talked to her friends
- **R** (Record) – yes, she used the TRAMm Tracker in the workshop
- **A** (Activity) – yes, she attended the conference
- **M** (Monitor) – yes, she intends to discuss what she learnt in her next supervision
- **m** (measure) – yes, her CPD certificate is evidence of her attendance.

While reading through the TRAMmCPD information, Sally notices that there is a website (www. TRAMmCPD.com), where there is information freely available for download. Keen to maintain momentum, she downloads the TRAMmCPD Information Pack, which includes blank TRAMm Trackers and Trails (Chapters 3–8). She also orders the *TRAMmCPD Handbook*. Using the TRAMm Tracker, she records brief details of her attendance at conference, ticking off the HCPC standards and all those relating to TRAMm.

Tasks

The following tasks encourage you to evaluate Sally's use of TRAMmCPD and identify your own learning needs to allow full engagement in the CPD process. You will find it useful to refer to your identified learning needs in order to develop a full profile, which will meet your CPD requirements as the chapters progress.

Is Sally's TRAMm Tracker a good example? To help you answer this question consider the following:

- Do you think Sally has made effective use of the TRAMm Tracker?
- Do you agree with the information she has entered? Has she really met HCPC standards –4 and visited every TRAMm station?
- Would you have included anything else?
- What would you do differently?
- Read Chapter 4 for more advice…

Now consider the following questions regarding your own CPD:

- What is your current approach to CPD? Which (if any) of the examples in this chapter do you identify with?
- Considering your current approach to CPD, as identified in the previous question, think how the TRAMm model could help you become more strategic.
- If you would like to follow Sally's example go to http://www.TRAMmCPD.com. Download the TRAMm information and record the details of your most recent CPD activities on the TRAMm Tracker.
- If you have not already done so, read Chapter 2 to identify your preferred learning style in order to help you identify the strategies that will be most effective for you.
- Now read Chapter 4 to learn more about how to plan and disseminate your learning (TRAMm station T for 'Tell').

TRAMm TRACKER　　　　　　　　　　　　　　　　　　　　**Name: Sally OT**

Date	Subject	Description	Certificate	Reflection	TRAMm Trail	HCPC Standards					TRAMm					Index	Notes
						1	2	3	4	5	T	R	A	M	m		
	Click here to enter text	Click here to enter text	☐	☐	☐	☐	☐	☐	☐	☐	☐	☐	☐	☐	☐		Click here to enter text
	Click here to enter text	Click here to enter text	☐	☐	☐	☐	☐	☐	☐	☐	☐	☐	☐	☐	☐		Click here to enter text
	Click here to enter text	Click here to enter text	☐	☐	☐	☐	☐	☐	☐	☐	☐	☐	☐	☐	☐		Click here to enter text
	Click here to enter text	Click here to enter text	☐	☐	☐	☐	☐	☐	☐	☐	☐	☐	☐	☐	☐		Click here to enter text
DD/MM/YY	Conference	Attended 2 day conference	C	☐	☐	1	2	3	4	☐	T	R	A	M	m	1	**Viewed poster display & exhibition stands, attended sessions: CPD certificate in CPD file item 1**

Figure 3.2 TRAMm Tracker: Sally's first attempt

4

How do you plan and disseminate your CPD?
TRAMm Station T: TELL

This chapter explains two essential aspects of communication in relation to CPD and is presented in two parts. Part 1 (Planning) will define what we mean by planning, discuss how to plan, and how to use supervision and appraisal/professional development reviews to help you identify your CPD requirements. It gives advice on how to decide on the most appropriate type of CPD for your needs and how to articulate your requirements. Part 2 (Dissemination) will highlight the importance of disseminating the outcomes of your CPD, and explore ways in which you can do this. It will demonstrate how to make the most of both written and verbal dissemination (including publications, presentations and workshops), emphasising how these can be designed and executed with few resources.

Tasks at the end of the chapter will encourage you to consider the potential output from your CPD, and how it related to your learning needs and the strategic direction of your organisation.

What do we mean by 'Tell' and why is it important?

Talking to others is an essential part of CPD – not only to discuss your own activities and future plans (planning), but also to learn about others' thoughts and ideas and inform them about the outcomes of your CPD (dissemination). The HCPC (2012c) highlights the importance of discussions with colleagues as a valid CPD activity. This is supported by Alsop (2013), who dedicates a whole chapter to ways of learning with others in her book *Continuing Professional Development in Health and Social Care*.

Talking to others can provide an active forum for learning and can help to keep you and others motivated. Alsop (2013) also emphasises the importance of having a sense of belonging and contributing to the whole organisation or community. This adds value to learning, thus providing greater satisfaction. Some people, particularly auditory learners, can find discussion useful as a way of consolidating their understanding and bouncing their plans or ideas off others.

It is important to note that 'Telling' is not only a verbal activity. Much dissemination makes use of the written (rather than the spoken) word – for example, through writing for publication, use of social media and providing project reports. Even in planning, we use the written word to articulate our planned activities through aims and objectives or goals, reflections and TRAMm Tracker and TRAMm Trail. Lloyd et al. (2014) found that a key enabler in workplace learning is having access to peers and 'learning networks', which again suggests the importance of communication in CPD.

Part 1: Planning

This first part of the chapter will explore potential communication channels and how they can be used to help you plan your CPD journey.

'Tell' and planning

Please don't assume that 'planning' only means that we expect you to sit and meticulously plan and document your goals/objectives/CPD journey down to the very last detail. Although planning can take place in a variety of ways, the more effective you are at planning, the more strategic you become in your approach to CPD. In a study to assess the impact of CPD for doctors in primary care, Mathers et al. (2012) found that if CPD was unplanned and was not linked to appraisals or organisational objectives or took place in isolation, there was less chance of it being implemented in practice. As we know, implementation is vitally important and is therefore classed as a mandatory component of CPD, according to the HCPC (2012c).

Planning may be formal or informal and some of the things we do often involve planning even though we are unaware that we are doing it. Part of the skill of planning is becoming consciously aware of when such planning is taking place; once this is clear, future planning skills can be developed or honed. Planning can relate to:

- Thinking about or articulating what you want to achieve in the next week or month
- Considering what you wish to achieve in the next year or the next 5–10 years
- Thinking about how you might achieve your goals and by when
- Giving opportunities full consideration when they arise
- Identifying clearly articulated SMART (Specific, Measurable, Achievable, Realistic, Timely) aims and objectives.

Whatever your approach to learning and working, it is also important to be flexible in your approach to planning. In Chapter 3 we outlined four different learning/working styles that people may recognise in themselves: the ostrich, the bull in a china shop, the procrastinator and the strategist. Some planning is better than none at all, and – as a starting point – planning for each of these approaches may be quite straightforward.

Examples of early stage planning

The ostrich

If you consider yourself to be 'an ostrich', your first goal might be to get your head out of the sand and access **www.TRAMmCPD.com** to remind yourself of the HCPC standards for CPD. You may also decide to download TRAMm Tracker and TRAMm Trail, which may be as far as your initial plans go. At this point, you may still have no idea where your CPD is heading. Your next move might therefore be deciding to discuss your lack of direction in your next supervision in order to clarify your thoughts and help you to explore possible options. You may also talk to some of your more organised peers to ask how they are approaching CPD and find out whether any of their ideas appeal.

The bull in a china shop

You may think yourself more like the bull in the china shop if you say yes to every possible CPD opportunity that presents itself. If this is you, your immediate goal may be to stand back and take stock of the relevance of each of your CPD activities and identify those that are most appropriate for your current role. At your next appraisal, you agree with your line manager on your core goals for the forthcoming year only; and any activities you choose will relate to these goals. You may find a TRAMm Tracker useful so that you can begin to index your CPD file, incorporating only the most relevant CPD you have undertaken.

The procrastinator (sitting on the fence)

If you are more of a procrastinator, you may find it difficult to make decisions and perhaps have a tendency to put things off until another day. Your plan will be to stop thinking and start doing. You could start by making a decision to use TRAMmCPD and agree one realistic goal with your line manager that you will be able to achieve by your next supervision.

The strategist

If you are a strategist, you are already well organised, with clear objectives that you have identified and documented in an appraisal or supervision log. This handbook will have been a considered purchase to enable you to further develop your skills using TRAMmCPD as a framework for your professional development.

Informal and formal planning

Planning can be undertaken in a number of ways but, particularly in the early stages of your career, talking to another person can enable you to articulate your thoughts and hear them reflected back, with or without advice on how to pursue your goals. This 'talking' can take place in both informal and formal situations.

Informal planning discussions

These are activities that may be formal or informal in nature and are not specifically designed to enable you to articulate your learning needs. Nevertheless, they may facilitate this by their very nature. Examples of informal discussion opportunities include:

- Talking with peers over coffee
- Networking with other professionals
- Discussion during staff meetings
- Peer group support
- Journal clubs.

A journal club, for instance, is designed for a group of people to discuss and critique new approaches to intervention. However, the subject of learning needs for individuals or the whole department might arise through this discussion, as can be seen in Example 4.1 below.

Example 4.1 Sanjeev (informal planning discussion)

Sanjeev, an art therapist, decided to co-ordinate a journal club for his colleagues in a community mental health team. As a team they are considering integrating co-production as part of their team philosophy. Each team member has been asked to identify one article that explores the effectiveness of co-production in a mental health setting. Following a discussion about the benefits of this for the team and the service users, Sanjeev has been asked how this might fit with his role as an art therapist. He realises that, due to a lack of understanding of co-production, he has not fully considered this. He has now identified this as one of his learning needs so that he can present it to the team in two months' time.

It is important not to underestimate such informal approaches, which provide an invaluable opportunity to air and debate your thoughts in a relatively unconstrained and therefore potentially more creative manner. To illustrate this, it may be useful to consider the most informal discussions you have had – for example, over coffee or lunch with colleagues, which may have prompted new learning opportunities or resolution of clinical dilemmas without attending a conference, course or supervision with a line manager.

Formal planning discussions

Formal mechanisms are those that are in place specifically designed for you to discuss progress and agree learning needs. They include appraisals or professional development reviews, and the use of supervision or mentorship. (Supervision and Mentorship are discussed in more depth in Chapter 7.)

Example 4.2 Sanjeev (formal planning discussion)

Sanjeev has weekly supervision as part of a comprehensive staff development programme within his community mental health team. At his most recent supervision, Sanjeev discussed his anxieties about the unit's plans to introduce co-production. His manager explored the core reasons for these concerns with him and two issues emerged: he was worried that this would not fit with his role as an art therapist; and had no other art therapist within the team to discuss this with. At the end of the supervision, he agreed two goals with his supervisor to be completed by the end of the forthcoming week:

- To find at least one article that comprehensively explores the concept of co-production and its implementation in a community mental health setting
- To contact his professional body to see whether there are any other art therapists working within a setting that has adopted co-production.

Sanjeev and his supervisor decide that this will be the focus of their discussion the following week. In preparation, Sanjeev has agreed to prepare a summary of what he sees as the key points about co-production, following his reading of the article. He also decides to reflect on how he sees co-production fitting with his role and where he thinks it may conflict with his role.

Considerations when planning

You need to consider several issues if your CPD planning is to be effective. These include issues relating to yourself, issues relating to the organisation in which you work, what resources are available to you, and possible fallback positions. These aspects are discussed in more detail below

Issues to consider in relation to yourself

In order to discuss your CPD learning needs and the reasons for these in an informed way, it is important to consider your baseline as measurement of CPD. This is becoming increasingly important (see Chapter 8), especially when trying to make a case for funding attendances at conferences and other training events. This baseline can be best mapped by thinking about where you currently are in your career, and the steps you have already taken to get there.

We recommend that you ask yourself the following questions:

- Are your plans realistic?
- Where are you now in your career?
- What skills and knowledge do you have? What have you already achieved?
- What skills and knowledge would you like to have? What would you like to achieve?
- Where do you see yourself in five years' time? What steps do you need to take to help you get there?
- What are your preferred learning styles?
- Which learning styles are you less comfortable with?
- What is the most appropriate way to address your learning needs, taking all these points into account?

Example 4.3 Sanjeev's personal learning needs

Sanjeev has been a qualified art therapist for two years and has spent his time since qualification working for the community mental health team, where he has built up considerable experience using art as therapy when working with people with anxiety and depression. This has given him a clear insight into the factors that can motivate or inhibit recovery.

He has already undertaken one small project in the workplace, which demonstrated the value of art as a means of expression with this group. He feels he now has a general idea of the core principles of co-production but is yet to fully reflect on how this relates to his role and the contribution he can make. He feels this is important, as he would like to remain a valued member of the team should they decide to move forward with this way of working. He is also aware that he is the only art therapist employed in this area who has experience of co-production and is keen that this should become an area of expertise for him. This would help with his future plans to travel abroad to work in an international community.

Sanjeev is an auditory learner, who is generally reflective in his approach. He would therefore prefer opportunities that allow him to discuss and reflect upon the implications of the issues explored. He also realises that part of his role will be to work as an activist if the co-production concept is adopted. Following discussion with his manager, he would therefore like to find out more about how he can help drive the implementation forward.

Issues to consider in relation to the organisation in which you work

Having considered your own CPD learning needs, it is also essential to consider those of the organisation for which you work. This is particularly important if you are hoping to use resources from your workplace to enable you to grow and develop. To help you with this, consider the following questions:

- What are the aims of the organisation in which you work now?
- What are their priorities?
- What is their attitude to CPD?
- Who is available for advice and support? If you don't know, how are you going to find out?
- Who do you need to approach to make your case for CPD?

Example 4.4 Sanjeev's workplace organisational priorities

It has been established that Sanjeev's organisation is keen to provide a mental health service that reflects the core principles of a recovery model, and respects the rights and opinions of service users in relation to their own rehabilitation. Despite this innovative outlook, there is no extra government funding available to support this co-production initiative. Sanjeev knows from the organisation's CPD policy that any professional development requirements will need to be supported by a good case, together with an indication of how any additional training may benefit the service and be supported financially.

Mindful that he will need to present his case to the Director of Therapies, he investigates a variety of funding opportunities outside the organisation and identifies a couple of organisations that are already applying this model. Sanjeev contacts two of the organisations for initial discussions to find out how co-production works in practice.

Issues to consider in relation to the resources available to you

Once you have considered yourself and your organisation, you can begin to think about the types of resources at your disposal and how to make the best use of them. These resources are not always immediately obvious and you may need to be creative in your thinking to maximise your options. This is where talking to others can be particularly useful. Issues to consider include:

- What financial resources are available to you within the organisation?
- What other resources are at your disposal? Who else can assist you?
- What other resources might you be able to utilise that are not immediately obvious?
- How much are you prepared to contribute yourself – in terms of time, money and effort?
- Who do you need to discuss and share your plans with?
- What types of activities are available to address your learning needs, and which are the most appropriate?

Example 4.5 Sanjeev talks to his colleagues to identify additional resources

Following initial discussions with the Director of Therapies, Sanjeev has established that there is a small staff development fund that provides limited funding for these purposes. There is no specific per capita allocation for each staff member so he is likely to have to compete for funding with other clinical staff in his team. As a member of a specialist mental health interest group, he is also entitled to apply for a small grant towards project development. The local co-production network offers regular free seminars, where people who have adopted this approach are encouraged to disseminate their successes and challenges.

Talking to his immediate colleagues, he realises that they are all in the same situation – all equally keen to develop their understanding of co-production and how it fits with their roles. As a team, they decide to pool their ideas and potential funding sources. They organise a co-production conference, inviting local experts, including service users. They agree that the best way to fund the event is to invite colleagues in other organisations and charge them a small conference fee. This will also provide a good collaborative approach, while allowing opportunities for Sanjeev to discuss his potential role with fellow art therapists in the region.

Sanjeev attends the evening co-production seminars in his own time and at his own expense. The Director of Therapies has agreed that the organisation of the conference can take place in work time as long as clinical caseload continues to be given priority. Sanjeev, together with his occupational therapy and mental health nurse colleagues, agree to share this responsibility.

Issues to consider if the situation changes or your plans change

Although the first part of this chapter has emphasised the importance of plans and discussing these with others, this does not mean that plans are rigid and cannot be changed or amended. On the contrary, it is very rare that plans do not change over time – for example, as a result of a change of clinical interest, change of job, change of manager, or change of life circumstances/unforeseen circumstances.

It is essential that alterations to your plans are not viewed negatively but instead seen as a positive opportunity to renegotiate your personal or professional direction. Sailing provides a good analogy for this. Initially, we plot a course to sail to a predetermined destination. We have taken into consideration the wind direction, tide, weather and leeway. Occasionally, due to a sudden, unpredictable change in wind direction, we have to steer to another course. At other times, we may review our journey's progress and decide we need to drop anchor for a while to consider how far we have come, enjoy our current position or even review the course we have planned to follow. Or we may decide to change our intended destination altogether, as a result of choice or necessity. None of these changes is wrong. Each decision is based on a series of carefully considered options, some of which may have resulted from intended or unintended circumstances.

If the situation or your plans change, or you simply change your mind, ask yourself:

● What has caused my plans to change? Is it me and my wishes/life events? Is it the people I work with? Is it the specialist/clinical area I am in? Is it the organisation?

● Is this situation temporary? (You don't want to make drastic changes to your plans if the issue causing you to rethink them is not permanent.)

● What possibilities are now open to me?

● What are the advantages and disadvantages?

● Where do I want to go now?

● What am I going to do next and how?

● What are my new goals?

Part 2: Disseminating

'Tell' and disseminating

There are various ways to disseminate the results of your CPD, the choice of which will depend largely on the type of information you want to disseminate, who your audience will be and for what purpose. Again, dissemination can be done informally or formally.

Informal dissemination

Informal mechanisms of dissemination usually happen on an ad hoc basis, with limited planning, forethought or structure. Examples can include:

- Office-based discussion
- Talking in the staff room/socialising
- Internal communication such as email
- Networking
- Social media.

The advantages of these types of communication are that they can relay information immediately and the subsequent discussion may often clarify or change ideas. The disadvantages may be that not everyone gets to know what is being discussed and this can lead to speculation or miscommunication of information. Another disadvantage is that informal discussions are often not recorded, and important information can be missed. This is where the TRAMm Trail can be useful to record brief details, including dates of informal discussions, and who they were with (see Chapter 5).

Although these are informal, mostly unplanned discussions, you still need to think about what you are saying and respect those you are communicating with. You must remain professional in your discussions/correspondence at all times; there are usually consequences for breaking protocols or procedures, even on an informal level.

Formal dissemination

Formal dissemination is that which has been strategically planned in some way. This often involves either written documentation or pre-organised feedback/presentation sessions where you need to send in an application beforehand or be invited by the organisers. The more formal arenas for disseminating your CPD include:

- Conferences/presentations
- In-service workshops/courses/roadshows
- Team exercises/away-days
- Peer-reviewed articles/books
- Projects/pilot studies/service developments reports

- Conference calls
- Social media
- Internal communication (such as intranet, email, staff newsletter)
- Team/preparatory/management meetings
- Supervision/annual appraisal.

Presenting at conferences

Conferences are a popular forum for formally disseminating work undertaken as part of CPD, including work innovations, research and project/service development. There are many important considerations to ensure that you select the most appropriate forum to disseminate your work.

Firstly, consider which type of conference you are going to submit an abstract for; this will largely depend upon your target audience. Conferences are run by a variety of organisations, which may include your professional or regulatory body, your own organisation, private companies, major exhibitions and international or European networks.

It is important to remember that the activity of presenting at a conference does not, in itself, meet all the HCPC standards. By using TRAMmCPD as a framework for your CPD, you will be able to identify areas that require further consideration. The work you are presenting may meet HCPC standards 1–4 but the act of presenting the work may only meet standards 1 and 2.

The types of things that you might do at a conference to formally disseminate your CPD include:

- Giving a keynote lecture
- Giving a presentation or presenting a paper
- Presenting a poster or a facilitated poster
- Giving an innovative technology presentation
- Running a workshop, seminar or round table discussion.

Giving a keynote lecture

As a keynote speaker, you are generally invited to present an aspect of your work for which you are renowned – either at a national or international level. Being an invited speaker is usually considered an honour, particularly at the larger external conferences. For this, you do not need to propose an abstract but will be expected to provide a short biography, an outline of your presentation and sometimes a copy of your speech for later publication.

Giving a presentation or presenting a paper

Presentations allow you to present information in front of a much larger audience than other types of forum. Timings vary enormously, depending on the particular conference, but the average duration is between 20 and 60 minutes unless you are presenting a paper.

Presenting a paper gives you an opportunity to present a very concise account of your work. Paper presentations are usually included as part of a themed session containing a further three or four papers on similar subjects and supported by a chairperson to guide the session. Usually a period of approximately 10–15 minutes is allocated for each uninterrupted presentation, plus a further 5 minutes for questions. Questions can either be asked at the end of each presentation or saved until a short panel question-and-answer session, following all presentations in the group.

In paper sessions, timing is usually very strict and you will be stopped by the chairperson if you go over your time. It is therefore extremely important to practise your presentation a few times to get it timed accurately – unless you already have expertise in this area. Copies of your slides, or the reference for a published directly related article, can be made available electronically or via hard copy. If you choose a paper presentation session you:

- Have a good way of introducing your work to a large audience in a concise manner
- Should expect to benefit from a few (mostly) constructive thoughts on your work, which will provide you with ideas to think about after the conference
- Have the opportunity to meet other interested people at the end of the paper session for further discussion or exchange of contact details.

Presenting a poster or facilitated poster

Within health and social care, as well as in commercial settings and other spheres of life, posters have an important role in informing and educating people. They have also become a popular alternative to presenting papers at conferences. If you also provide an A4 copy of the poster for delegates to take away with them, people can think about the material and contact you at a later date. Facilitated posters provide an opportunity for you to present (usually for about 5 minutes) and discuss your poster with a small group of delegates and fellow poster presenters. Posters have many advantages. They:

- Reach a large number of people
- Can be placed in a wide variety of settings
- Can be used over a long timespan
- Allow the reader to consider material at their own pace
- Give information for less literate people (using images and clear phrases)
- Give information in a non-invasive manner (no stigma)
- Should convey information in an attractive, eye-catching fashion
- Allow for creativity in structuring information
- Allow readers to question and discuss the content if the exhibitor is present.

Giving an innovative technology presentation

If you have designed and produced equipment, software, training materials, videos or communication aids, this gives you a chance to showcase and share these innovations with fellow professionals and obtain immediate feedback. If you choose this option, conference organisers should provide you with space to enable you to provide demonstrations, present a video, or show the product in question. A small visual display area is usually available, along with a tabletop area for you to demonstrate your ideas, although you will usually need to provide your own equipment. The benefits of innovative technology presentations are that they:

● Provide an ideal forum to showcase your innovation in front of a relatively captive audience

● Provide an opportunity for people to see how the innovation should work, possibly try it for themselves and also to ask questions.

Running a workshop

These enable you to pass on your skills to others. Each workshop usually lasts for around 90 minutes and is limited to approximately 20–30 participants. Workshops may be related to practice, management, theory, education or research and development. Ideally, you need to allow time for some 'practical' work, such as practising a skill, discussion groups and trying out tools. You will usually be responsible for chairing and facilitating the session. The benefits of workshops are that they:

● Provide time for skill practice and development

● Allow time for questions and clarification

● Allow a much greater amount of time for discussion and explanation

● Are usually attended by like-minded people to allow exploration of ideas

● Provide an opportunity for people to trial and critique your work.

Running a round table discussion

An interactive discussion (maximum usually approximately 20–30 participants), which enables you to present topics for interactive debate with delegates. Round table discussion sessions usually last for approximately 45–60 minutes, giving plenty of time to debate the topics and get input from delegates working in similar areas. You will usually be responsible for chairing and facilitating these sessions. Although most of the session will be based around audience participation, its success will depend largely upon the trigger used and facilitation of discussion so it is important to give careful consideration to this and engage a co-facilitator if you think this is not your strength. Round table discussions are a good choice if you:

● Have an interest in a hot topic that requires further discussion and debate

● Would like to generate a consensus opinion from a group of colleagues

● Require a short period of focused discussion time with other interested people.

Running a seminar

Seminars are presenter-led sessions, where you have the opportunity to present your topic and allow questions to be raised within the session time. You will usually be responsible for chairing and facilitating the 40–60 minute session, which is based on a certain amount of audience participation but usually less than a round table discussion or workshop. A seminar is a good option to choose if you are looking for a forum that:

- Offers time to present your work in more detail than during a paper presentation
- Allows participants to question and clarify key issues and principles
- Provides an opportunity for you to canvas general opinion.

Applying to a conference

When you are writing and submitting an abstract for a conference, you should consider the following:

- What are you going to submit an abstract about and, if appropriate, who with?
- Who is your target audience?
- Review the overall theme of your work, and select the most appropriate conference.
- Alternatively, find out the theme of your selected conference and write your abstract accordingly.
- Note the date and venue in your diary. If you submit an abstract, they will expect you to attend and present.
- Consider where you plan to get funding from (to pay for transport, accommodation and registration) or do you intend to fund your attendance yourself?
- Ethical approval evidence is necessary for all research so ensure that you have this readily available.
- Which presentation format will be most appropriate for what you wish to present?

When you write the initial abstract, it is probably wise to complete all the relevant information in a Word document, following the headings and word count instructions. Then you can cut and paste the final information directly into the electronic submission system, ensuring that you have first spell-checked the information and checked it through carefully. As you are writing, it is important to:

- Remind yourself of the conference theme
- Read and ensure that you adhere to the conference guidelines for submitting an abstract, making a note of submission procedures, deadlines and acceptance notification dates.
- Provide a clear title and concise list of contents that meets abstract guidelines
- Ensure you have correctly referenced your abstract, in terms of style and numbers

- Ask someone to check it
- Include a brief biography, if required.

Preparing for a conference

Once your abstract has been accepted and you are preparing for the conference:

- Ensure that you adhere to your abstract and the timings. Have you covered everything you have said you will, in the way you have stated you will? For example, if you are presenting a paper, remember it is just that.
- Ask someone to proofread your presentation or poster to eliminate any errors.
- Consider what you will do if the technology fails on the day. What is your back-up plan?
- If you are presenting a poster, how will you get it printed?
- Consider the layout of the room you have been allocated for your presentation.
- Are you going to provide handouts?
- Are you going to have an attendance sheet?
- Will you encourage audience participation and questions throughout, or ask them to wait till the end?
- How does the technology work? You may need to get there early to set the room up as you want, if appropriate.

Tips for audiovisual aids

- You only need the equivalent of four to five bullet points on each slide (prompts only)
- Use cue cards if required
- Practise running through the slides
- Use a combination of relevant pictures and text
- Be consistent in style
- Avoid the use of inappropriate material and take care with cartoons
- Ensure that you (or someone else) check your slides or poster
- Reference your material appropriately and adhere to copyright legislation
- Ensure that the material on the slides is clearly linked to what you are saying.

Tips – verbal skills

- Speak clearly
- Project your voice
- Practise your presentation

- Ensure that you can pronounce all words/names
- Do not make it too complicated
- Use a microphone if one is available
- Do not waffle; be clear and to the point
- If there is something you do not understand, leave it out. Don't try to be clever.

Tips – non-verbal skills

- Stand up
- Check where you are in relation to what you want the audience to be looking at
- Look at the audience or at the back of the room
- Don't wear anything distracting or have anything in your pockets.

Pitfalls – audiovisual aids

- Too much text on the slides or poster
- Slides too busy or too many effects
- Spelling and grammatical errors
- Plagiarism
- Visual material not clearly related to the verbal presentation.

Pitfalls – verbal skills

- Speaking too fast or too slow
- Speaking in a monotone
- Mumbling or speaking too quietly
- Reading from the slides or from sheets of paper
- Being unable to pronounce key words or names.

Other pitfalls

- Poor timing – making your presentation too short or too long
- Not knowing how to use any props
- Using inappropriate material for the target audience
- Having a poor flow in your material
- Trying to be too clever with your information
- Making things up when you don't really know the answer.

And finally

You know more than anyone about what you are presenting but…

- You may not know everything about the subject – others might know more than you

- Be prepared to accept constructive ideas and suggestions and learn from them

- Have a few phrases ready for those who may challenge you aggressively – for example, 'that's a very interesting idea, perhaps we can discuss it further after the presentation'.

Writing for publication

The written word can be a very powerful way of disseminating information and it allows you to reach a much wider audience than some of the spoken formats highlighted earlier. Written material can be available for reference at a time that is convenient for the reader and has more chance of being cited accurately (although when reading documents, articles or books, it is always important to scrutinise the material with a critical eye). However, the main disadvantage is that written material can often be out of date by the time it is published, particularly if peer review is involved. Information can often take 18–24 months from initial thought to publication and sometimes takes even longer. This delay is partly due to the peer review process, but journals often have themed editions so the editor may hold your article back until the most appropriate edition.

When writing for publication, as with conferences, it is important to think about your target audience. There is a vast range of journals and publishers and careful consideration is required in order to reach the people who are likely to be interested and can make best use of the information. If you decide that the CPD information you have to impart is best suited to a text, identify a range of relevant publishers and look online to see what kind of texts they publish.

When considering other media, you should aim to get your work published in peer-reviewed journals if possible, as these generally reach a wider readership and are considered more credible. If you think a journal may be more appropriate, then it may be useful to visit your organisation's library (or if you have no library, visit the local university or public library) to explore the range of journals available that reflect your topic and target audience. Bear in mind that there is a hierarchy of journals, which is measured by something called 'the impact factor'. This refers to the level of credibility and the expected number of citations and is particularly useful to consider if you are in education and being entered for research assessment. Select a few of the most relevant journals and then look at the types of articles they include and select one that matches your intended style.

When starting your paper, make sure you read the publication guidelines carefully and have them close at hand at all times. All journals are different and it is especially important to take note of the structure (which varies according to the type of article), word count and referencing style. If you don't follow the guidelines, your paper is very likely to be rejected, or you will be required to address the issues anyway.

Most professional journal editors prefer rigorous, ethically approved research so some material may be more suited to professional news magazines, organisational newsletters or web-based reports. Do not be disheartened if your work is not considered suitable for journal publication. This does not mean that it is not valuable and that people do not want to hear about it. In fact publishing in other documents can be just as valuable; you get your message out there in a succinct way and it can be a great way of networking and promoting your expertise to others. Check out your professional news magazine or specialist interest group and see what is published there. If you are unsure whether your topic will be of interest, contact the editor or group chairperson (usually listed at the front of the journal or on the website home page). They will often be happy to have a chat about their requirements.

Using social media

For those interested in using technology, social media is a way to enable and encourage social interaction. Web-based and mobile applications 'enable people to create, engage and share content' (Davies et al. 2012, p. 1). There are many and varied forms of social media which, when used wisely, can be a valuable addition to your CPD. Technology is widening the scope of CPD and encouraging interaction between groups of people by enabling and encouraging the sharing and dissemination of news, information, ideas, resources and advice. Social media can provide a versatile and accessible platform for providing support, and communicating your thoughts, ideas and best practice, along with the opportunity to engage in professional discussion and critical debate (Maclean et al. 2013, Bodell & Hook 2011).

The use of social media to interact with others can help avoid feelings of isolation, and encourage interaction, collaboration and knowledge sharing. It offers an opportunity to promote greater awareness of your role, build new relationships and connect with individuals and organisations, both locally and globally. In a recent publication, the HCPC highlights the fact that the building of informal, professional networks plays an important role in encouraging and retaining competence, as well as improving practice, and should be encouraged and fostered (HCPC 2015a, p. 46). Engaging in social media can provide access to a range of key people such as service users, carers, ministers, NHS executives and others (Holdsworth et al. 2013).

It is important to maintain professionalism and adhere to the HCPC's and your professional body's and employer organisation's codes of conduct and guidance at all times, in both professional and private interactions.

For more information on social media as a CPD activity, see Chapter 6; and for ways to record your social media activities for evidence, see Chapter 5.

Tips on using social media

- Many formats are free to use.
- Check your professional body for 'how to guides' such as *The College of Occupational Therapists Introduction to Social Media* (COT 2015).

- Ensure that you have read and adhere to the HCPC Focus on Standards: Social Networking Sites (HCPC 2015b)
- Ensure you have read and adhere to your professional body guidance on the use of social media.
- Ensure you have read and followed your employing organisation's guidance on the use of social media.
- Talk to others who already use social media and ask them for advice.
- Remain professional in all your online interactions, whether professional or personal.
- Remember that anything you post will be a permanent record that is available for anyone to read. If you are in any doubt, do not post.
- Ensure that your privacy settings are used appropriately.
- Maintain service user confidentiality and anonymity at all times.
- Start slowly, and see what others are doing to get a 'feel' for which formats you are more comfortable with. Most sites are happy for you to 'lurk' in order to understand and follow how others are interacting.

Organising a roadshow

Roadshows give you an opportunity to showcase something you have developed or wish to promote in order to generate interest outside your organisation. A roadshow is also an opportunity to generate information or feedback. For example, as an educationalist you may be designing a new Master's programme for health professionals; the roadshow will allow you to present your initial ideas to a range of people from different areas and receive feedback to ensure that you are meeting the needs of your potential applicants. The TRAMm model had its own roadshows when it was initially developed, in order to recruit people to trial its use and comment.

Running in-service training

In-service training is usually undertaken by the organisation's staff, for the staff of the same organisation. It is a really effective way of disseminating feedback from CPD; it is usually free of capital costs and, more importantly, it is a way of giving something back to an organisation which (in most cases) has supported you by giving you time and sometimes funding for CPD. In fact, you may suggest running some In-service training as part of your case for attending the CPD in the first place (see Chapter 6). In-service training can take a variety of forms and may include things like skills workshops, case studies or other general feedback presentations, journal clubs and storytelling sessions. It may just be a short lunchtime presentation, a full day, or more.

Sometimes in-service training may be organised internally for staff of the organisation and non-staff members can attend if they pay a small fee. This may be a way of generating further CPD funds for staff, and can again be a good 'output' to include when you argue the case for your CPD.

Case study: Sally learns to discuss and disseminate her CPD through supervision

In Chapter 1 we introduced Sally, an occupational therapist who attended a two-day conference with little planning or organisation. At the end of the second day, she participated in a TRAMmCPD workshop, where she was introduced to the HCPC standards for CPD and the TRAMm model and decided that she needed to become more strategic in her approach to CPD. In Chapter 2, Sally identified her learning styles and realised that she should participate and engage in activities to allow learning to occur and to further develop her reflective skills. The following case study continues from Chapter 3, after Sally has familiarised herself with TRAMmCPD and initiated her TRAMm Tracker.

Sally attends supervision with her manager (who you will remember is a physiotherapist and has not yet heard of TRAMmCPD). Sally takes her completed TRAMm Tracker (see Figure 3.2) to discuss what she has learnt at the conference, how she intends to use TRAMmCPD to record her CPD and identify her future learning needs. Having looked at Sally's TRAMm Tracker, her manager asks how attending the conference and the TRAMmCPD workshop means that Sally has met HCPC standards 1, 2, 3 and 4 and how it has benefited her service users. Sally's manager is unclear about the TRAMm stations, from Sally's explanation, and asks her to undertake a 30-minute presentation of TRAMmCPD to her colleagues at the next monthly allied health professional team meeting. This will include occupational therapists, physiotherapists, a podiatrist, a speech and language therapist, a dietician and a social worker.

The planned actions Sally agrees to do before her next supervision are to:

- Amend her TRAMm Tracker to accurately reflect her achievements in relation to HCPC standards and TRAMm (see Figure 4.1)
- Present what she has learnt about CPD and TRAMmCPD to her colleagues – she can then provide actual evidence for Station T (Tell)
- Start planning for her rotation into neuro-rehabilitation and consider how a TRAMm Trail might help her with this, in preparation for her next supervision (see Figure 5.6, p. 77).

Sally agrees a time and date to present TRAMmCPD. She emails the presenters of TRAMmCPD, whose contact details are on the handouts she was given at conference, to ask for a copy of the PowerPoint. She downloads and prints off a TRAMm Tracker and TRAMm Trail for everyone. She then sends an email inviting her colleagues to attend a TRAMmCPD lunchtime presentation. After this, it is suggested that those who are interested agree to meet every two months for a lunchtime CPD meeting.

Tasks

The following tasks encourage you to consider the potential outcome from your CPD, linked to the learning needs you identified in Chapter 2 and the strategic direction of your organisation. You should also think about how these how all these aspects might be linked to each other.

- Think about your most recent piece of CPD. How could you disseminate the information to your colleagues or other people in your organisation?

- In your next supervision, can you arrange to discuss your plans? If you do not have a supervision process in your workplace, how can you ensure that you have someone to talk through your CPD plans with? Do you need to set one up?

- If you have not already done so, download a TRAMm Tracker from www.TRAMmCPD.com and begin to record your most recent pieces of CPD.

- Initiate a TRAMm Trail (available for free download from www.TRAMmCPD.com) for your most significant piece of recent CPD and focus your attention on Station T for that specific CPD activity. If you have nothing to record in this section, think about what you can do to rectify this. Remember to record the dates and to continue to update your TRAMm Trail (see Chapter 5 for details about what to include).

- Do you agree with the information Sally has recorded in her TRAMm Tracker? Would you have recorded something different? Why?

Read on to Chapter 5 to learn more about ways of recording your CPD (TRAMm station 'Record').

TRAMm TRACKER   Chapter 4: *amended tracker*   Name: Sally OT

Date	Subject	Description	Certificate	Reflection	TRAMm Trail	HCPC Standards 1	2	3	4	5	TRAMm T	R	A	M	m	Index	Notes
	Click here to enter text	Click here to enter text	☐	☐	☐	☐	☐	☐	☐	☐	☐	☐	☐	☐	☐		Click here to enter text
	Click here to enter text	Click here to enter text	☐	☐	☐	☐	☐	☐	☐	☐	☐	☐	☐	☐	☐		Click here to enter text
DD/MM/YY	Conference Workshop	**TRAMm Model for CPD with overview of HCPD standards**	☐	☐	☐	1	2	☐	☐	☐	☐	R	A	☐	☐		**TRAMmCPD TRAMm Trail initiated (Date). Trail stored on CPD usb.**
DD/MM/YY	Conference	**Conference Day 2** (This learning has been split to acknowledge two separate learning events. See entry above)	C	☐	☐	1	2	☐	☐	☐	☐	☐	A	☐	☐	1	**Attended Stroke Rehabilitation Seminar; TRAMmCPD workshop. CPD certificate of attendance in CPD file.**
DD/MM/YY	Conference	**Attended 2 day conference**	C	☐	☐	1	2	☐	☐	☐	☐	☐	A	☐	☐	1	**Viewed poster display & exhibition stands, attended sessions: Professional use of social media.**

Figure 4.1 Sally's amended TRAMm Tracker

5

How do you record your CPD plans and activities?
TRAMm Station R: RECORD

This chapter explores why it is important to record your CPD and the mechanisms by which CPD can be recorded, including personal and professional development plans, learning contracts, reflections/reflective models and portfolios. It will also illustrate how the TRAMm Tracker and TRAMm Trail tools can be used to clearly record the CPD undertaken. We will introduce the TRAMm Tracker as a recording tool and show completed examples of both the TRAMm Tracker and the TRAMm Trail.

Tasks at the end of the chapter will encourage you to consider the most effective ways to record information – ways that reflect your own learning and retrieval styles. Development of a portfolio format will be suggested, and you will be encouraged to complete at least one reflection using a reflective model template and one record using the TRAMm Trail.

What do we mean by 'Record'?

Recording is the process of capturing data in written or other permanent form, for the purpose of preserving evidence (*Oxford English Dictionary* 2007). There are many different ways to record data, both formal and informal. Suggestions for items you might include in your Station 'R' Record are listed in Table 3.1 (p. 27). Whatever you record for your CPD, you must remember to protect the anonymity of service users and stakeholders, and ensure that anything submitted for HCPC audit or shown to another person remains completely confidential (HCPC 2012d).

Why do we need to record CPD?

It is your responsibility as a professional to initiate, undertake and record your CPD. The HCPC Standard 1 (HCPC 2012a, p. 4) states that registrants must maintain a 'continuous, up to date and accurate record of their CPD activities' and 'keep a record of CPD, in whatever format is most convenient'.

In addition, the HCPC and all the registered health and care professional bodies provide members with a code of ethics and professional conduct that outlines your responsibility as a registered professional for actively maintaining and continuing your professional development and for retaining a record of your CPD.

From your own perspective, regardless of guidelines, it is an important part of evidencing your development over time and receiving credit for the things you have achieved. It is also intrinsically rewarding to have a record showing that you have made a difference to the lives of service users and students through your professional career.

How and when should we record our CPD?

In Chapter 2 we discussed the uniqueness of each individual in terms of preferred working and learning styles and the same applies to recording CPD. If you are a visual learner, you are likely to prefer recording mechanisms that provide a visual snapshot of your learning, such as the TRAMm Trail, TRAMm Tracker or a mind map. If you are a read/write learner, you may prefer to undertake a written reflection and first, and fill in your formal record later, once you have decided what you have learnt.

There are so many different ways to record your CPD and it is a question of personal preference whether you use traditional pen and paper or an electronic recording method. Online technology appears to be a popular method these days, as it is convenient to store, and quick and easy to update as you progress. This form of recording keeps evolving and now includes media such as videos, voice recordings and e-collation methods.

Various methods of recording your CPD are explored in more depth below.

Reflective logs

Reflection is the process of analysis, critical awareness and self-evaluation that results in a change of practice. It allows us to learn from our experiences and plays a large part in the development of knowledge and skills (Constable 2013). Chapter 6 highlights how reflection can be undertaken as a CPD activity and Chapters 7 and 8 explore the use of reflection in the monitoring and measurement process. In this chapter, we look at the ways in which we can record our reflections.

There are several formats for keeping reflective logs, including use of a structured template for supervision, written accounts following a specific reflective model, and the use of social media such as 'blogging' or weblogs (see p. 63).

Reflective logs are exploratory, self-critical accounts of a process or critical event. Their aim is to explore the reasons why something has happened and what influenced the outcome. They can also help you identify how things could be done differently, from both an objective and subjective perspective. This may not only include description and evaluation of the process or event but can also involve exploration of emotive aspects such as your own (or others') feelings, values and attitudes, which may have contributed to the outcome. Reflective logs should always lead to either a change or validation of practice. Any actual changes to practice, together with their impact, can be added to the log at a later date.

Various models can be accessed to facilitate written reflections and the selection of model is very dependent upon personal preference and reflective style. All have similar criteria but they differ in their emphasis and the terminology they use. Examples include:

- Schon (1983): Reflection in and on action
- Gibbs (1988): Reflective cycle, six stages – description, feelings, evaluation, analysis, conclusion and action plan
- Boud (1988): Follows a three-stage process – returning to the experience, attending to the feelings and re-evaluating the experience
- Johns (1994): Nuances of reflection; involves a series of questions that help structure the practitioner's reflections, supervision and keeping of a structured reflective diary; designed as a reflective nursing model but questions can be adapted to other fields
- Fish and Twinn (1997): four strands of reflection – 1. factual strand (what happened); 2. retrospective strand (looking for patterns and meaning); 3. sub-stratum strand (exploring assumptions/values/feelings); and 4. connective strand (implications for practice and plans)
- Rodgers (2002): four-stage reflective cycle – presence, description, analysis and experimentation.

If you are want to explore any of these models further, references are provided at the end of this book.

Mind maps

Mind maps provide a visual tool with which to organise your thoughts around a subject (see Figure 5.1, p.60). They are a useful way to record a brief summary of your CPD in relation to a specific topic and identify links between relevant areas. They also provide a one-page snapshot that can act as a catalyst for discussion in supervision or mentorship sessions (see Chapter 7).

Mind maps usually contain less detail than the TRAMm Trail (see example p. 77) but a little more than the TRAMm Tracker. They can therefore act as a useful bridge between the two, to act as a reminder of what you have achieved. You can then return to your mind map later in order to jog your memory for your TRAMm Trail and reflections. There are websites that provide mind map templates, which may be worth exploring in the first instance.

Figure 5.1 applies the mind map concept to the content of this chapter and its connections to other chapters in the book.

Learning contracts

Learning contracts are collaboratively written and agreed documents that indicate what will be learnt, the resources to be used, and how the learning will be evaluated and evidenced or validated. They offer a concise way of explicitly recording learning needs in relation to a specific context. These contracts are often used by students on placement, when they have generic learning outcomes specified by their university that need localising to their placement setting.

They can be considered as working documents. During their completion, it must be clear exactly how the learning need will be demonstrated and who will validate each piece of evidence.

A useful template is shown in Table 5.1 (page 61).

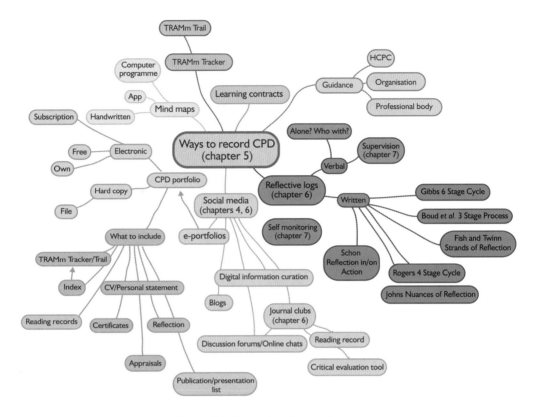

Figure 5.1 Example of a mind map

Compiling portfolios

A portfolio is a collection of evidence designed for a specific purpose and organised in a specific way. In the same way as an artist, photographer or designer produces a portfolio to showcase their ability, we too can develop portfolios that showcase our professional ability through our CPD.

Portfolios are confidential documents, either in hard copy or electronic format, which you can choose to share with others in full or in part. They can be for your own personal use or compiled for a particular purpose (Blogg & Challis 2013) such as job interviews. When organising your portfolio, you can also have 'public' and 'private' sections, where the private section is easy to remove if necessary. A portfolio is *not* the same as the profile that you are expected to complete as part of your HCPC audit (see Chapter 8).

You can take various approaches to compiling your professional portfolio but the important factor is to remember that it should represent you and what you have achieved. It is much better to have one portfolio with content entirely produced by you, rather than three or four enormous files containing leaflets, instructions, reports and articles written by other people, with very little reflection or 'real' evidence of your CPD and how it has influenced your practice and your own and others' performance.

Table 5.1 Example of a learning contract template

Learning need (What do you want to learn?)	Resources (What resources can you utilise to help you to learn?)	Evidence (How can you show you have achieved what you set out to learn?)	Validation (Who will confirm your evidence and when?)
1. How to undertake my CPD and what evidence to provide for it	Text: Hearle, Lawson and Morris (2015). *A Strategic Guide to CPD for Health Professionals: The TRAMm Model* TRAMm Trail TRAMm Tracker Colleagues portfolio examples	Portfolio format designed by: DD/MM/YY Undertake 1 TRAMm Trail for an element of CPD Complete relevant sections on the TRAMm Tracker	Line manager in supervision: .... TRAMm mentor via online support: .... TRAMm mentor via online support: ....
2. Models of reflective practice	Internet/databases using search terms: Reflective models, Portfolios in healthcare	Two written reflections using models accurately: One following Gibbs' model of reflection and the other following Boud by: DD/MM/YY	Line manager in supervision: ....

Content to consider including in your CPD portfolio

This is a list of the sort of things you might consider including but it is not exclusive. Remember to anonymise service users or other sensitive information.

Introduction to your CPD and portfolio:

● TRAMm Tracker or another continuous, up-to-date and accurate CPD record

● You may also require an index if you are not using a TRAMm Tracker.

Introduction to you:

● Your Curriculum Vitae

● A personal statement

● List of your publications and presentations (see Chapter 4).

Evidence of your CPD:

● Learning contracts

● Appraisals

- Supervision and preceptorship records
- TRAMm Trails
- Reflections on your practice/courses/significant incidents
- Other creative reflective work, such as stories, poems or diary excerpts
- Reading record
- Intervention evidence records (see Chapter 8)
- Evidence of additional responsibilities (such as supervision of students) or advanced practice following the four pillars, i.e. practice, management/ leadership, education and research, especially if you are aiming for more senior promotions (see NLIAH 2010)
- Summaries of research or evaluation reports, alongside a reflection on your contribution to them
- Summaries and reflections on roles within your professional sphere such as professional body activities, external examining and interprofessional roles
- Summaries of roles outside your professional work that you have undertaken (or that you are currently undertaking), together with a critical commentary on their application to your current work. For instance, if you are a tennis coach or teach photography in your spare time, this may be very relevant.

Other evidence of your CPD:

- Certificates
- Details of any awards, with descriptions of the awards
- Testimonials
- Anecdotal evidence (see Chapter 8).

Organising your CPD portfolio

It is personal preference how you choose to organise your CPD portfolio but you must remember that it needs to be accessible, logically ordered, functional and easy to update. You can design the structure yourself, follow your professional body's guidance or utilise an online portfolio builder. The other way to organise your portfolio is to use TRAMmCPD to provide a framework to organise the contents.

A well-structured CPD portfolio enables you to present and access information easily for job or other applications, interviews, discussions at appraisal, HCPC audit and accreditation exercises.

Online methods of recording

There are more and more methods available to record evidence of your online interactions, which may contribute to your CPD. Some of these may be developed and accessed via your professional bodies, others by paid subscription to private companies. Other forms of social media (such as e-portfolios, digital curation tools, information collation tools and blogs) are available at little or no cost. They provide the opportunity to disseminate information, document your thoughts, share ideas, store useful information and advertise your role or service. Whichever method you use, you must always exercise caution and follow the guidelines (set out by the HCPC, your professional body and other organisations) regarding the use of social media and online recording.

Weblogs (known as blogs) offer a way to record your personal observations, reflections, opinions and thoughts on a website, many of which are free to use. Some sites allow you to keep your blog private, or invite selected people to view what you have written, or make it freely available to the public. Reading other people's blogs can also give you useful information but, as with all social media, caution is required as they are not peer reviewed and care must be taken when interpreting or using any information from them (Moorley & Chinn 2015).

Online information collation tools enable you to capture, as a transcript, your online conversations and even allow you to make further comments. To fully utilise these tools, some time and skill are required. It may be possible to use links to your collation tool as part of your evidence of CPD. Alternatively, a quicker, simpler option may be to take screenshots of your discussions as proof of your interactions, if required.

If you choose to participate in discussion forums, online chats and/or online journal clubs, record your participation in your TRAMm Tracker, including dates with relevant links. For most significant sessions and interactions, you could initiate and update a TRAMm Trail, including what you contributed to, where to access the information in the future and how you have used the information you have learnt.

For online journal clubs to be most effective as a CPD activity, you should ensure that you select relevant chats in which to participate, critically evaluate the article using an appraisal tool, complete a reading record, and write or record a reflection to show how you will apply what you have learnt. You could also consider whether you can disseminate (Tell) what you have learnt to your colleagues and the most effective way to do this (see Chapter 4).

A record of your social media activity may provide useful evidence for your CPD. Many of the social media activities you have engaged in will be freely available online, and the HCPC may accept links to your social media activity if it is relevant to the CPD profile you are submitting. For major pieces of evidence, it is worth considering printing your social media evidence in order to provide the HCPC with hard copies.

A document by NHS Employers (2013) provides further useful guidance regarding the use of social media. It is essential to remember that the popular platforms of social media are constantly changing and it is important to choose your options wisely. You must also ensure that you observe and adhere to all the professional guidance regarding the use of social media and remember that there is no distinction between private and work life when you are a registered health or care professional. Be very careful about what you (or your friends and colleagues) post about you and ensure that your privacy settings are activated.

For more on using social media as 'Tell', see Chapter 4; and as an 'Activity', see Chapter 6.

Using the TRAMm Tracker and TRAMm Trail to record your CPD

TRAMmCPD encompasses the TRAMm model, TRAMm Tracker and TRAMm Trail. (The TRAMm model and its development are discussed in Chapter 3.) The TRAMm Tracker and TRAMm Trail have been developed as tools to complement the TRAMm model and help you engage with and record your CPD (Morris *et al.* 2011).

The TRAMm Tracker (see Figure 5.3, p. 73) has been designed as an adaptable tool to record and measure individual learning outcomes, while taking into account the HCPC standards for CPD. The TRAMm Tracker allows you to track your progress, and offers you the ability to record, monitor and measure your professional development as you journey towards fulfilling the HCPC registration standards. The TRAMm Tracker also enables you to cross-reference your learning between each station, identify gaps in your learning needs and index your CPD file.

The TRAMm Trail (Figure 5.4, see pp. 74/5) enables you to plan and record in a little more depth the most significant pieces of your CPD, which you may need to use if you are called for HCPC audit. It has been designed following the feedback we have received, as a brief summary of work and learning, to be used alongside your favoured method of reflection. It is also a useful, easy-to-complete document that can be referred to later when completing reflections. Feedback from the pilot evaluation suggests that people have found it most effective to use both their TRAMm Tracker and TRAMm Trail as 'works in progress', updating them as they go along. They have also used them in their supervisions and annual appraisals to highlight what has been achieved and identify future learning needs (see Chapters 7 and 8). Some people use a weekly or monthly alarm to remind them to update their TRAMmCPD; this has been referred to by one participant as their own personal TRAMm nagger!

How and when should you use the TRAMm Tracker and TRAMm Trail?

This chapter focuses on the TRAMm Tracker and TRAMm Trail as methods of recording your CPD. Chapter 8 will highlight how they can be used to measure your CPD. The TRAMm Tracker is used to record the things you have already achieved, whereas the TRAMm Trail can be used to record your plans and thoughts about things you intend to do, as well as to record in more depth the things you have already achieved or done.

The TRAMm Tracker enables you to briefly record in one place all the CPD you have achieved, and it can be submitted to the HCPC as part of your evidence (respecting confidentiality). To decide what to record on your TRAMm Tracker and Trail, it is important to recognise when routine work has developed into CPD (see Chapter 3). This is when you notice that you have stopped working on 'automatic pilot' and you are employing an activity (see Chapter 6) in order to learn something new. Your usual intervention has had an unintended consequence and/or you have been asked to undertake something new, of which you have little or no experience. You may have reflected on the reasons for this and the changes required to your practice as a result. Through supervision or appraisal, you may have identified a new way of working or perhaps you are beginning to develop advanced skills in order to further your career. You may have attended a training event in the past and you may have recently used the knowledge gained to improve your practice and a service user's outcome.

At any of these points, a new entry (or an update to an existing entry) in your TRAMm Tracker may be needed. It is entirely up to you when to initiate or update a TRAMm Trail. You may decide to do it because you realise you have too much information to record briefly in your TRAMm Tracker or perhaps you recognise that there is significant learning taking place, which needs to be recorded in more depth. It must be stressed that the TRAMm Trail is to be used alongside your favoured method of reflection to fully record your learning and outcomes. Mapping your usual work activity into TRAMmCPD could highlight that you are, in fact, developing your practice and your activities have crossed over into CPD. This is then worth recording in more depth.

The HCPC document *How to Complete your Continuing Professional Development Profile* (HCPC 2012e) provides full details of what you are required to submit for audit (see Chapter 8). The HCPC do stress that you should use whatever method works for you, all activities must be dated and that everything you submit must be your own work. It is important to remember this when using your TRAMm Tracker, as the most common issues in the HCPC audit feedback (2014b) are that registrants fail to supply dates, do not differentiate between work and CPD activities, fail to number/label pages, and focus on quantity rather than quality. The HCPC (2014b) advise that you only choose between three and five activities from the last two years to use as evidence. This is useful to remember when reflecting on your CPD. The TRAMm Tracker enables you to identify, at a glance, all your CPD that meets the four HCPC standards and visits all the TRAMm stations. From these, you can choose which pieces to provide as detailed evidence.

How to complete your TRAMm Tracker

This is available as a free download from www.TRAMmCPD.com.

As discussed earlier, the decisions about which TRAMm stations each piece of your CPD visits are entirely subjective, although some suggestions are included at the beginning of Chapters 4–8. The TRAMm Tracker is designed to be used as a working document, to be initiated and added to over time. It is not anticipated that you will necessarily meet each HCPC standard or visit every TRAMm station for every piece of your CPD. Initially, you may only complete HCPC standards 1 and 2 and visit TRAMm station A (Activity) but, as time passes and you use what you have learnt, you can revisit and update your TRAMm Tracker. It is important to date every entry, as the HCPC recommends at least one CPD activity every two months. They also ask for explanations if there are gaps of three or more consecutive months (HCPC 2015c).

If you look at the TRAMm Tracker, you will see that Figure 5.2 (page 72) provides an outline of page 1 and a brief overview of the five HCPC standards, along with some suggestions for each of the TRAMm stations. *Remember*: by keeping an up-to-date TRAMm Tracker, you will be meeting HCPC Standard 1, and Standard 5 is only met if you are called for HCPC audit. Figure 5.3 (page 73) provides an outline of page 2 of the TRAMm Tracker. You may also note that the example TRAMm Trackers have the most recent entries at the top of the form; this enables you to quickly add new entries without scrolling through the whole document. However, you are of course entirely free to arrange your TRAMm Tracker as it suits you.

Remember that the Tracker is only designed to provide an 'at-a-glance' index record of all CPD undertaken and achieved, whether formal or informal. Sometimes it can be difficult to decide whether you need to add an additional row in the Tracker or to expand one that is already started. For example, let's say you attend a course on designing the environment for people with dementia and log this on your Tracker. During your work with a service user with dementia, you subsequently realise that you need more information on the types of equipment that would be useful in the bathroom. You therefore contact a colleague in a local dementia unit, who has the required expertise, and arrange a visit. Is this a new CPD activity or just a continuation of the original one? The decision is yours, as long as the information is documented. In this situation it is more likely that you would continue with the original Tracker row, as the activities are clearly linked, and it would allow you to complete additional columns for the TRAMm. Alternatively, you could choose to start a new line and log the link between the two in the notes column, as Sally decided in Chapter 4 (Figure 4.1, p.55).

Table 5.2: The TRAMm Tracker: A brief overview

Page/Column	Content
Page 1	Overview of the five HCPC standards, along with suggestions for each of the TRAMm stations.
Page 2	The TRAMm Tracker
Column 1: Date	Date(s) event/activity took place (state if ongoing)
Column 2: Subject	Brief title of CPD activity carried out
Column 3: Description	Brief description of event/what you did
Columns 4, 5 and 6: Certificate, Reflection and Trail	Record whether you received a Certificate of Attendance, have written a reflection and/or initiated a TRAMm Trail about the event.

Column 7: HCPC standards	Enter which of the HCPC standards you feel are met by each CPD event. Initially you may only meet Standards 1 and 2. As time passes and you carry out more work/learning, you may revisit your Tracker and complete more standards. It is not expected that every piece of your CPD will meet all HCPC standards. You will find more information in the HCPC publication (2012c) *Your Guide to our Standards of CPD*.
Column 8: TRAMm stations	Enter which TRAMm stations you feel you have visited for each CPD event. Initially you may only visit the 'A' (Activity) station. As time passes and you carry out more work/learning, you may revisit your Tracker and complete more stations. It is not expected that you will visit each station for every activity or piece of CPD (see Chapters 4–8 for more information regarding each station).
Column 9: Index	This column relates to the index in your CPD file/portfolio, where each piece of hard evidence is stored. If your evidence is stored electronically there is space for this in your column 10 notes. There will not always be a need to record anything in this column.
Column 10: Notes	This column is for you to record your own notes on items that you feel are most relevant – for example, cross-references to Key Skills Framework (KSF) standards, workplace competencies, where you have stored information, where to find other related pieces of evidence, where the event took place and with whom, etc.

Some questions you could ask yourself in order to make the decision include:

1. Does it link directly to the same learning need as the main row? (If not, start a new row.)

2. Is it a very distinctive new activity, such as a course? (If yes, start a new row.)

3. Have I learnt or done very different things in this new CPD activity? (If yes, start a new row.)

4. Is the notes column too full and lacking in clarity? (If yes, start a new row or initiate a TRAMm Trail to record more information.)

5. Is what you are trying to record becoming confusing or unwieldy? (If so, initiate TRAMm Trail(s). You may need to separate out the learning events. For example, Sally's record of conference attendance in Chapter 3 has been separated into conference day 1, conference day 2 and TRAMmCPD workshop attendance.)

For significant pieces of CPD, to plan your future learning needs or to provide a reminder, you may wish to record details in a little more depth using the TRAMm Trail or other recording mechanisms such as reflections.

The TRAMm Tracker was originally developed to encourage you to maintain a continuous up-to-date record of your CPD. However, after the twelve-month pilot evaluation feedback, it became apparent that it was difficult to remember why certain columns had been completed. The TRAMm Trail was then developed as a method to plan future development and CPD activities and also as a way to record learning/activities that have taken place in more depth. The 'Plan of Action' section enables registrants to record their future plans, identified from their Tracker and Trail.

The TRAMm Tracker and TRAMm Trail can also be used when preparing for job interviews and annual appraisals by helping you identify the most relevant pieces of CPD and decide which CPD evidence is most pertinent to the job or role for which you are applying.

How to complete your TRAMm Trail

The TRAMm Trail has a dual purpose. It can be used to strategically plan your CPD to achieve your outcome: what it is you want to achieve and how you are going to get there (see Figure 5.4 below). The TRAMm Trail can also provide a method to record in a little more depth the most significant pieces of your CPD, which you may use if you are called for HCPC audit. The Trail has been designed to provide a brief summary of work and learning, to be used alongside your favoured method of reflection.

The TRAMm Trail has a section for each of the TRAMm Stations (Tell, Record, Activities, Monitor and Measure), together with a 'Plan of Action' section (see Chapters 4–8). You can document as little or as much as you wish, and record it according to your preferred style (such as words, pictures, captions or cartoons) to remind you what you plan to achieve, with timescales, or what you did and when. Remember, it is vital to include dates and where to find the evidence if it is required. On some occasions, you may decide that the same piece of evidence or learning needs to be recorded in more than one TRAMm station. For instance, your appraisal might be included in TRAMm 'T' as a discussion of your learning needs, 'R' as a written record, and alongside 'm' as a successful measure of your professional achievements.

Like the TRAMm Tracker, the TRAMm Trail is designed to be used as a 'work in progress' to update regularly and keep as a working document. It can then act as a prompt, alongside your favoured method of reflection. Once completed, the relevant TRAMm Trails can be submitted as evidence if you are called for HCPC audit.

Avoid trying to record too many learning experiences in one TRAMm Trail, as this can become confusing. If this is the case, it may be advisable to break the learning/event down and use more than one Trail.

Example 5.1 India's use of TRAMm Tracker and TRAMm Trail

India (a student dietician) recorded her eight-week placement, along with the case study she presented to her educators, in one line of her TRAMm Tracker and the details in one TRAMm Trail. She found that her Tracker and Trail became very lengthy and she was becoming confused between what was placement learning and what was specific to the case study. She was advised to break the learning into two separate but linked entries on her TRAMm Tracker and TRAMm Trails, as follows:

● TRAMm Tracker entry/Trail 1 – An overview of the whole placement experience, where she recorded what she had learnt, including brief reference to the case study she presented.

- TRAMm Tracker entry/Trail 2 – Case study: A more detailed record of the learning carried out with the service user, including the assessment, planning, intervention, outcome process and the self-directed informal research she carried out into the medical condition, alongside the skills learnt to use a slideshow presentation programme to present the case study. India also completed a written reflection.

Table 5.3 The TRAMm Trail: A brief overview of sections and suggested contents

Section	Suggested content
TRAMm Trail title	Link your title to columns 2 and 3 in your TRAMm Tracker.
Date	Date that you initiated your TRAMm Trail; remember that each entry should include a date where relevant and/or note that work is ongoing.
Tell (T)	Record relevant Tell – conversations and discussions: with whom, who you disseminated information to, etc. (See Chapter 4 for more details.)
Record (R)	Written record of evidence – when and where the evidence is stored. (See Chapter 5 for more details.)
Activities (A)	List of relevant activities completed, with dates. (See Chapter 6 for more details.)
Monitor (M)	List of your monitoring activities – whether constructive feedback or self-critique. (See Chapter 7 for more details.)
measure (m)	Outcomes achieved/measurement of meeting HCPC standards/visiting TRAMm Station m. (See Chapter 8 for more details.)
HCPC standards met	Enter which HCPC standards you believe this piece of CPD meets. Update as necessary over time.
Plan of action	What do you plan/need to do next? As you achieve these aims, they can be moved to the relevant station section.

In your TRAMm *Trail*, it is likely that you will visit other stations to record your thoughts about what you plan or intend to do. By planning you are completing an 'A' (activity) and by working on a Trail you are making an 'R' (record). As you carry out your plans, undertake your activities and achieve your goals, you can begin to complete more of your TRAMm *Tracker*, recording what you have achieved.

As an example, consider Sally's TRAMm Tracker (see Figure 5.5, p.76) and her TRAMm Trail, entitled 'Rotation into neuro-rehabilitation' (see Figure 5.6, p. 77). In her TRAMm Tracker she has ticked 'A' because she is carrying out the 'activity' of planning what she intends to do next but she has not actually completed her plans. She has also marked 'R' because she has initiated a TRAMm Trail to make a 'record' of her plans. In her TRAMm Trail, however, she has written and recorded her plans in every TRAMm station. The entries in italic type are the plans she has made. As she achieves each one, she will remove the italic type and then complete the relevant corresponding column in her TRAMm Tracker.

Case study: Sally uses TRAMm Tracker and TRAMm Trail to record her CPD

In Chapter 1, we introduced Sally (an occupational therapist) who attended a two-day conference, where she participated in a TRAMmCPD workshop, after which she decided that she needed to become more strategic in her approach to CPD. In Chapter 2, following identification of her learning styles, Sally realised she should participate in activities for learning to occur and needed to further develop her reflective skills. Having familiarised herself with TRAMmCPD and initiated her TRAMm Tracker in Chapter 3, she has started to use TRAMmCPD in supervision to help identify and articulate her CPD plans. In Chapter 4, she began to engage in ways of planning and disseminating her learning.

One of Sally's identified needs during supervision in Chapter 4 was to start planning for her rotation into neuro-rehabilitation. In preparation for her next supervision, Sally initiates her first TRAMm Trail, which includes a record of the things she thinks she needs to do towards her forthcoming rotation.

With her supervisor, Sally records the outcomes of her supervision, including a set of negotiated and agreed goals, as follows:

1. To learn more/recap her neuroscience anatomy knowledge, using publicly available online video learning material, and understand its relevance for practice; to be explained to her supervisor at the next supervision session.

2. To understand the application of neuro-developmental approaches in preparation for practice. (As Sally is not yet in neuro-rehabilitation, she is not sure how to make this 'live' but she makes a few notes and decides to take it to a second pre-meeting with her prospective new line manager and makes an appointment to meet with her again before starting.)

3. To speak to a Band 5 who is rotating away from neuro-rehabilitation at the next peer support group; to discuss with other Band 5s what they have done that was useful.

4. To investigate the NICE guidelines and care pathways for Stroke and document the relevant aspects for her role as an occupational therapist.

5. To investigate further training opportunities for neuro-rehabilitation.

6. To reflect upon her anxieties about rotating into a specialist area and discuss this at her next supervision.

7. To initiate a TRAMm Trail, to record in more detail her attendance at the TRAMmCPD workshop at the conference, and to update it as she uses what she has learnt (see Figure 5.7, p.78).

Following her supervision, Sally updates her TRAMm Tracker to include a reference to presenting TRAMmCPD at the Allied Health Professions meeting. She completes the additional HCPC standards and TRAMm stations she has met, and initiates a TRAMm Trail (see Figure 5.6, p.77) for her forthcoming rotation. She also records a written reflection using her preferred model, which is currently that of Gibbs (1988).

Sally realises that she is now building up a useful record of her CPD activity and that she needs to develop a portfolio in order to house and organise her records. She still has the one she developed at university and decides to retrieve this from her loft, look at how it was structured and decide if this is the way she needs to continue. While looking through this portfolio, she removes all the out-of-date information, retaining only material that is still current (such as certificates of academic qualifications and her merit award for practice education at university). Sally's CV will need updating before it is included and the rest of the information is archived. She has not yet decided how to structure her portfolio and therefore uses the current system to file her new Tracker, Trail and supervision logs.

Sally has now updated her TRAMmCPD entry from Chapter 4 (see Figure 4.1, p. 55) on her TRAMm Tracker to reflect her achievements and plans. As can be seen from her Tracker, she has decided to split conference day 2 into two separate areas of learning, as she was struggling to identify which standards and TRAMm stations she had met/visited. On the TRAMm Trail for her rotation into neuro-rehabilitation, Sally decided to enter her plans alongside those aspects she has already achieved, using italics to distinguish her plans from her achievements. As her plans are fulfilled and completed, she can easily update her Trail by removing the italics and changing the wording from future to past tense.

Tasks

The following tasks will encourage you to consider the most effective ways to record information, reflecting your own learning and retrieval style. Development of a CPD portfolio format will be suggested and you will be encouraged to complete at least one reflection using a reflective model template and one record using a TRAMm Trail.

1. Choose a reflective model that you are less confident in using and complete one reflection for your most recent significant piece of CPD.

2. If you have not already done so, download a TRAMm Tracker from www.TRAMmCPD.com and begin to complete it for your most recent pieces of CPD.

3. If you have not already done so, download a TRAMm Trail from www.TRAMmCPD.com and begin to complete it for your most significant piece of recent CPD. (Remember to record in the 'Plan of Action' section when you will update your reflection.)

4. If you have already initiated a TRAMm Tracker and/or TRAMm Trail, remember that they have been designed to be used as 'working' documents, to be completed and updated regularly as your learning progresses. Are you able to add to your TRAMm Tracker and/or TRAMm Trail? Have you identified further learning needs? Will you discuss this in your next supervision? Read Chapter 7 for further information.

5. If you already have a CPD portfolio, look at how it is structured to see if it is the most effective way to organise your material. If you are happy with it, go through each of the sections and remove/archive any information that does not relate to the last two years, with the exception of information that is always relevant, such as academic qualifications or evidence of specialist/advanced practice/courses.

6. If you do not already have a CPD portfolio, investigate the available options and begin to set one up.

7. If you do not already know, find out when your next HCPC audit dates are from http://www.hpc-uk.org/registrants/cpd/dates/

8. Read Chapter 6 to discover more about the range of activities available for your CPD (TRAMm station A 'Activity').

Standard 1	Standard 2	Standard 3	Standard 4
Maintain a **continuous, up to date and accurate** record of CPD activities	Demonstrate CPD activities are a **mixture of learning activities relevant** to current or future practice	Seek to ensure that CPD has contributed to the **quality** of their practice and service delivery	Seek to ensure that CPD benefits the **service user**

Standard 5 - Only applies when called for HCPC audit

Upon request, present a written profile of own work, supported by evidence, which explains how standards have been met

TRAMm STATIONS – *Suggestions only*

TELL (Chapter 4)	RECORD (Chapter 5)	ACTIVITY (Chapter 6)	MONITOR (M) (Chapter 7)	mEASURE (m) (Chapter 8)
Informal/Formal Discussions with colleagues/Meetings	Publications	Research/Project work	Formal/Informal Mentorship	Appraisal/Specific Individualised Goals
Planning in supervision	Service Evaluation/Benchmarking	Learning from colleagues Tell	Supervision	Performance Indicators
Disseminating Information	Mind Maps	In Service Training	Peer reviews	Letters of Commendation/Awards
Training/Roadshows/Away Days	Written Reflections	Reading Journals/Books/Journal clubs	Formative Assessment	Standards of Proficiency
Presentations/Conferences/Courses	Learning Contracts	Attending Conferences/Courses	Student Educator	Audit
Providing feedback from CPD	CPD Record Sheet/Portfolio	Shadowing/Secondments/Rotation	Self-Monitoring through Relection	Outcome Measures
Annual Appraisals/Personal development review	CPD Certificates of Attendance	Informal/Peer Group Support		Skill Acquisition and Improvement
Sharing Case Studies	Annual Appraisals	Further Education		Updated Reflections
Social Media	Online Digital Curation	Active member of professional body		Peer Review
Pilot/Projects/Evaluation reports	Written documents/leaflets	Self-directed Learning		Preceptorship
Verbal reflection	TRAMm Tracker and Trail	E-learning/Social Media		Research/Quality Improvement Projects
	Curriculum Vitae	External Examining		

Figure 5.2 TRAMm Tracker, page 1: HCPC standards and TRAMm Stations

TRAMm TRACKER

Name:

Col 1 Date	Column 2 Subject	Column 3 Description	Certificate	Reflection	TRAMm Trail	Column 7 HCPC Standards					Column 8 TRAMm					Col 9 Index	Column 10 Notes
						1	2	3	4	5	T	R	A	M	m		
	Click here to enter text	Click here to enter text	☐	☐	☐	☐	☐	☐	☐	☐	☐	☐	☐	☐	☐		Click here to enter text
	Click here to enter text	Click here to enter text	☐	☐	☐	☐	☐	☐	☐	☐	☐	☐	☐	☐	☐		Click here to enter text
	Click here to enter text	Click here to enter text	☐	☐	☐	☐	☐	☐	☐	☐	☐	☐	☐	☐	☐		Click here to enter text
	Click here to enter text	Click here to enter text	☐	☐	☐	☐	☐	☐	☐	☐	☐	☐	☐	☐	☐		Click here to enter text
	Click here to enter text	Click here to enter text	☐	☐	☐	☐	☐	☐	☐	☐	☐	☐	☐	☐	☐		Click here to enter text

Figure 5.3 Blank TRAMm Tracker, page 2

TRAMm Trail

Please note: The TRAMm Trail has been designed for you to plan and record in a little more depth your most significant pieces of CPD. It is not anticipated that you would complete this for every piece of your CPD, only those you feel may be useful for evidence if called by the HCPC for audit. Remember to maintain confidentiality.

TRAMm Trail Title: Chapter 5: Strategic CPD Plan
Date: DD/MM/YY

These are suggestions, you are not expected to include all of these and you may have other items more relevant to you

Tell (T)	Record (R)	Activities (A)
• Who do you need to share your plans with? Will this be formally or informally? • Who will you disseminate information to and how? Locally/nationally/globally? • Verbal reflection? Who with? • Who and how will you disseminate your learning? • Informal and/or formal mechanisms? • Other? (Include dates these will be achieved by)	• Written Reflection? Which model and method of reflection? • Presentation? Leaflet? • Case notes? • CPD portfolio updated? • Curriculum Vitae updated? • Job application? • Social media? • TRAMm Tracker initiated/updated? • TRAMm Trail initiated/updated? • Business plan? • Learning Contract? • SWOT Analysis? • Mind map? • Other? (Include dates these will be achieved by)	• What are you going to do? What is your plan? • Have you identified any relevant training events/journal articles/conferences/social media opportunities? • Who do you need to contact? How are you going to find their contact details? • What do you need to set up or put in place? • What information is already available to you? Where is it? If not how will you access it? • Mixture of learning activities (HCPC Standard 2)? • Other? (Include dates these will be achieved by)

TRAMm Trail

Please note: The TRAMm Trail has been designed for you to plan and record in a little more depth your most significant pieces of CPD. It is not anticipated that you would complete this for every piece of your CPD, only those you feel may be useful for evidence if called by the HCPC for audit. Remember to maintain confidentiality.

Monitor (M)	Measure (m)	HCPC Standards met: (standards you aim to achieve)
• What are you going to measure? • How will you measure your progress? • What is your baseline? • Have you achieved what you set out to achieve or has the outcome been different than anticipated? Positive or negative. Have you reflected on this? • What would you do differently next time? • Will this learning contribute to the quality of your practice/service delivery? (HCPC Standard 3) • Will this learning benefit your service user(s)? (HCPC Standard 4) • Other? (Include dates these will be achieved by)	• What are you going to measure? • How will you measure your progress? • What is your baseline? • Have you achieved what you set out to achieve or has something changed? Has the outcome been different than anticipated? Positive or negative. Have you reflected on this? • What would you do differently next time? • Will this learning contribute to the quality of your practice/service delivery? (HCPC Standard 3) • Will this learning benefit your service user(s)? (HCPC Standard 4) • Other? (Include dates these will be achieved by)	**PLAN of ACTION:** • As you work through the TRAMm Stations what points have you identified need to be carried out next? • What would you like to achieve next? • Where may/will this learning event lead? • Update TRAMm Tracker (timescale) • Update TRAMm Trail (timescale) • Review and update Reflection (timescale) • What are you going to do next? • Other? (Include dates these will be achieved by)

Figure 5.4 Strategic TRAMm Trail

TRAMm TRACKER Chapter 5: updated tracker

Name: Sally OT

Date	Subject	Description	Certificate	Reflection	TRAMm Trail	HCPC 1	2	3	4	5	TRAMm T	R	A	M	m	Index	Notes
DD/MM/YY	Self-directed Learning	Rotation into Neurological Rehabilitation	☐	R	T	1	2	☐	☐	☐	☐	R	A	☐	☐		See TRAMm Trail: Rotation into Neurological Rehabilitation. Stored on CPD usb
DD/MM/YY	Preceptorship	Preceptorship completed	☐	☐	☐	1	2	3	4	☐	T	R	A	M	m		All documentation stored in Preceptorship file
DD/MM/YY	Conference workshop	TRAMm Model for CPD with overview of HCPC standards	☐	☐	T	1	2	3	4	☐	T	R	A	M	m		TRAMmCPD TRAMm Trail initiated (Date) Trail stored on CPD usb and updated (ongoing)
DD/MM/YY	Conference	Conference Day 2	C	☐	☐	1	2	☐	☐	☐	☐	☐	A	☐	☐	1	Attended Stroke Rehabilitation Seminar, TRAMmCPD workshop. CPD certificate of attendance stored in CPD file
DD/MM/YY	Conference	Attended 2 day conference Day 1	C	☐	☐	1	2	☐	☐	☐	☐	☐	A	☐	☐	1	Viewed poster display, exhibitor stands, attended session: Professional use of Social Media

Figure 5.5 Sally's TRAMm Tracker. Entries in green highlight updates from previous chapter.

TRAMm Trail

Please note: The TRAMm Trail has been designed for you to plan and record in a little more depth your most significant pieces of CPD. It is not anticipated that you would complete this for every piece of your CPD, only those you feel may be useful for evidence if called by the HCPC for audit. Remember to maintain confidentiality.

TRAMm Trail Title: Chapter 5: Rotation into Neurorehabilitation   **Date: DD/MM/YY**

Tell (T)	Record (R)	Activities (A)
• Discussed preparation plans for rotation into Neuro-rehabilitation with existing supervisor DD/MM/YY • Discuss with colleagues on Stroke Unit requesting any useful reading, assessments used and information about the new most up to DD/MM/YY techniques by DD/MM/YY • Discuss with band 5 who is completing her 6 month rotation in Neuro Rehabilitation by DD/MM/YY	• Supervision record (DD/MM/YY) • TRAMm Tracker updated (ongoing) • Initiate TRAMm Trail by DD/MM/YY • Notes will be taken from NICE guidelines, Care Pathway and COT Guidance noting any questions to ask once rotation has commenced stored on usb by DD/MM/YY • Write Reflection using Gibbs Cycle of Reflection about forth coming rotation by DD/MM/YY and update in six months' time	• Attended Stroke Rehabilitation session at Conference on (DD/MM/YY) • Arrange to visit neuro rehabilitation ward and meet manager/colleagues by DD/MM/YY • Recap and identify gaps in knowledge of neuroscience anatomy (ongoing) • Revise Neurodevelopmental approaches from university handouts by DD/MM/YY • Download latest NICE Guidance and National Care Pathway regarding Stroke by DD/MM/YY • Download the latest College of Occupational Therapists (COT) Guidance on Stroke by DD/MM/YY • Investigate further training available for Neurorehabilitation by end of month

Monitor (M)	Measure (m)	HCPC Standards met:1, 2
• Review aims and objectives set (DD/MM/YY) • Review Strategic plan trail with Supervisor at next supervision (DD/MM/YY)	• Future supervision records will identify increased confidence, knowledge and skills in this area • Positive feedback from service users/carers	**PLAN of ACTION:** Note: entries in italics are what Sally is planning to do.

Figure 5.6: Sally's TRAMm Trail: Neuro-rehabilitation

TRAMm Trail

Please note: The TRAMm Trail has been designed for you to plan and record in a little more depth your most significant pieces of CPD. It is not anticipated that you would complete this for every piece of your CPD, only those you feel may be useful for evidence if called by the HCPC for audit. Remember to maintain confidentiality.

TRAMm Trail Title: Chapter 5: TRAMm CPD **Date: DD/MM/YY**

Tell (T)	Record (R)	Activities (A)
• Reviewed aims and objectives set (DD/MM/YY) • Reviewed Strategic plan trail with Supervisor at next supervision (DD/MM/YY) • Future supervision records will identify increased confidence, knowledge and skills in this area • Positive feedback from service users/carers • Informal discussion with colleagues about CPD and HCPC requirements (DD/MM/YY – ongoing) • Presented TRAMmCPD to AHP colleagues and CPD support group set up (DD/MM/YY) • Formal discussion with Manager in Supervision (DD/MM/YY)	• Emailed TRAMmCPD requested copy of presentation and to be added to their contact list (DD/MM/YY) • Copy of TRAMmCPD Presentation and Trackers and Trails in CPD file (Index no) • TRAMm Tracker initiated (DD/MM/YY) • TRAMm Trail updated (DD/MM/YY) • Supervision record (DD/MM/YY) • Written reflection using Gibbs Model of Reflection (DD/MM/YY) • Organise CPD portfolio (ongoing) • Update CV (ongoing)	• Conference Day 2: Attended and participated in TRAMmCPD workshop (DD/MM/YY) • Practiced completing a TRAMm Tracker and TRAMm Trail (DD/MM/YY) • Revisited Conference Abstract Book for TRAMmCPD contact details. Abstract book stored in filing cabinet • Downloaded TRAMmCPD Information Pack from website (DD/MM/YY) • Downloaded HCPC (2012b) Our Standards for your CPD (DD/MM/YY) • CPD peer support group set up (DD/MM/YY)

Monitor (M)	Measure (m)	HCPC Standards met:1, 2, 3, 4
• Formal discussion with Manager in Supervision (DD/MM/YY) • Self-monitoring and review of progress (ongoing)	• Conference Certificate of Attendance in CPD file (Index no) • Positive feedback from Manager regarding well organised portfolio and her new approach to CPD (DD/MM/YY) • Positive feedback from colleagues re presentation (DD/MM/YY)	PLAN of ACTION: • Update Reflection in 6 months • Update TRAMm Tracker weekly • Update/initiate TRAMm Trail for significant CPD • Buy TRAMmCPD book for more information

Figure 5.7 Sally's TRAMm Trail: TRAMmCPD

6

What counts as CPD?
TRAMm Station A: ACTIVITY

This chapter discusses the types of activities that can be considered as CPD and how to maximise their impact. Individuals often engage in activities that contribute towards their professional development without realising they are undertaking CPD – for instance, learning from the advice of colleagues, being on a committee, undertaking long-arm supervision, researching current projects, reading a journal, external examining and attending conferences. This chapter advises you on how to decide on the most appropriate type of CPD activity for your needs. It is not intended to be a full 'how to guide'; rather, it will help you consider and select the most appropriate forms of activity and investigate their use and potential as part of your self-directed learning.

Tasks at the end of the chapter will encourage you to consider those activities you have already undertaken that have had the most impact on your CPD, and reflect on why this has been the case.

What do we mean by 'Activity'?

In this context, 'Activity' refers to something undertaken in order to facilitate CPD. CPD often starts with an activity, although this is not always best practice, as explained in Chapter 4 ('Tell'), where we have illustrated the importance of beginning by thoughtfully planning your own professional development needs.

There are numerous types of activities that can be used as part of professional development and these may include:

- Liaising with other professionals/agencies
- Training activities beyond mandatory and specialist training
- Learning from colleagues
- Undertaking your own research

- Reading journals or joining journal clubs
- Shadowing/secondments/rotation
- External examining
- Gaining accreditation, approval or revalidation
- Undertaking reflection
- Pursuing further education
- Doing project work
- Getting involved with your professional body
- Being an active member of a specialist section or interest group
- Undertaking preceptorship (or its equivalent)
- Attending conferences or courses
- Participating in workshops.

The HCPC (2012a) provides a list of ideas for possible CPD activities under the following headings: Work-Based Learning, Professional Activity, Formal/Educational, Self-Directed Learning and Other. They expect registrants to make professional judgements as to the appropriateness, context and frequency of activities in order to meet the minimum CPD standards. For the purpose of this chapter, these headings have been considered and reflected in sub-groups as follows: Formal Opportunities, Work-Based Learning, Professional/External Activities, Professional Support, Training, Informal Support, Social Media, Self-Directed Learning and Reflection. Remember that all activities can be useful CPD but you need to consider the context in which you are going to apply them, as the learning outcomes from CPD will vary according to each individual.

It is important to note that some of the activities discussed below may fit in with more than one TRAMm station, or more than one of the chapter sub-groups, listed above. The decision as to where your activities fit is entirely your own and may depend on the context in which they are undertaken and your own preferences. These lists are not exhaustive, and you may undertake many other things that you decide to use as evidence of your CPD.

Why do we need to undertake activities and how do we choose what to do?

Although the main reason for CPD highlighted by HCPC (2012a) is to ensure that registrants are fit for practice and meet minimum standards, it is important for professionals to think beyond minimum standards. For practice to develop, practitioners must consider which activities will help them to develop higher-quality practice and the additional skills they may need to influence quality provision (such as higher-level communication skills, entrepreneurial and management skills, research skills and the ability to teach others). As a practitioner, you should not only be undertaking the activities required to do your current job, but those that will enable you to do it to the best of your ability or make it possible for you or others to undertake other tasks in the future.

In Chapter 2 you explored the ways in which you could identify your preferred learning styles and the reasons why this was important when considering your choice of CPD activity. There are many different types of activities that can allow you to develop, both professionally and personally, and provide evidence of your learning. The following section gives some examples of the wide variety of activities you could undertake, together with suggestions for measuring their success and how they may count as CPD.

Formal activities

An important and invaluable method of achieving CPD is via formal activities such as education, research and project work. These activities not only further your own professional development and allow potential for promotion, but they can also contribute to the advancement of the profession and the growth of evidence-based practice in service delivery.

Research

Research skills, like any other aspect of practice, are on a very long continuum. At one end of the scale, there are undergraduate projects or small-scale service evaluations; at the other end, there are the sophisticated systematic reviews and large-scale, funded, randomised, controlled trials.

Health and care professionals from all backgrounds must be consumers of research but not all are required to be researchers. However, you do have a responsibility to ensure that practice and overall service delivery are evaluated so that you learn from best practice and strive to develop areas that need further improvement (see also 'project work' below).

In order to participate in research, you do not need to secure the funding or be the principal investigator (project lead). In fact for early researchers this is often not possible, particularly for the larger projects. Instead you may just form part of the overall team contributing to one small part of the project, such as data collection. You can also attend formal training to develop your own skill in this area (see pp. 82, 88).

If you are a more advanced researcher, you may already have some idea of how to put a bid together. If not, seek help from your local research and development board, professional body, university or local library service or even from your university colleagues. A good site to get you started is the Health Research Authority (HRA), at www.hra.nhs.uk

Project work

Although project management has been mentioned in research above, it covers many different aspects, including small-scale service development projects, introducing new policies and undertaking specific quality improvement projects. Projects are being initiated all the time, particularly in the health and care environments, but it can be difficult to get involved in leading or being part of the project team unless you actively seek opportunities.

Small-scale project management is a great way to develop your overall management skills, and if your project is successful it can provide evidence to use for your CV and for applications for promotion. If you are new to project management, there are also short courses that may help you to develop these skills. These courses may be provided on an in-service basis or externally (for instance, by your organisation or your local university). If you have managed small projects before but wish to take on something a little more complex, formal training could include courses such as PRINCE 2 methodology.

Formal educational study

There are a great many formal educational opportunities such as higher education degrees, Open University courses, distance learning modules or skills-based courses. For further information, investigate opportunities available at local universities or further education colleges, or search online for distance learning courses.

How can you measure the success of your formal learning opportunities?

For most formal learning opportunities, measurement is an easy process, as there is usually a clear outcome such as a certificate, project report or qualification. This is one reason why these types of opportunities are a popular form of CPD.

Research provides CPD by:

- Expanding your knowledge and skills in relation to the research process
- Encouraging you to read/critique articles and other literature on current practice, then develop conclusions to be disseminated and integrated in practice
- Developing data collection and analysis skills, which may be transferred into practice (e.g. narrative analysis or interviewing and service evaluation or improvement projects)
- Developing project management skills
- Helping to increase your understanding of the roles of other professionals (especially if working on a collaborative project) and thus providing opportunities for greater networking and more effective team working in practice.

Project work provides CPD by:

- Developing your skills and your understanding of change management
- Giving you experience of team working
- Helping you learn about financial management
- If interdisciplinary, it may help you to understand the roles of other professionals

- Giving you experience of managing a team, including leadership, delegation and negotiation
- Familiarising you with project planning and developing SMART objectives
- Improving your advanced report writing skills
- Enabling you to develop applications for funding.

Formal educational study provides CPD by:

- Offering you many benefits, which very much depend on the type of learning undertaken, and may include any of the above suggestions.

Mapping formal opportunities to TRAMm stations can be very easy if the activity is fairly short and simple. For a long course or project, you may decide to split the activity into sub-sections because you learn something different at each stage. (For instance, on your degree you may undertake a management module that teaches you one set of skills to apply, and then undertake a research module that provides you with others.) Formal educational study can be easily measured in terms of outcome. However, additional aspects (such as reflection or evaluation of how effectively your learning has been applied in practice) may need further explanation.

An example of this could be a research project that has demonstrated the effectiveness of a new intervention. Research is often undertaken in controlled circumstances so your additional measurement may evaluate how this has been implemented in normal day-to-day practice.

Informal activities

Less formal activities include worked-based learning and journal clubs.

Work-based learning

Work-based or workplace learning 'refers to CPD that is stimulated by and occurs through participation in workplace activities' (Lloyd et al. 2014, p. 1). Put simply, working and learning occur simultaneously, and work-based learning is considered essential for high-quality care and a popular choice for CPD, especially when there is limited funding for formal opportunities or training.

Work-based learning does not usually require any formal application to access, and it can provide very clearly focused development of knowledge and/or skills specifically related to your workplace. These can include activities such as shadowing (learning alongside an expert colleague), secondments (periods of time spent working within another role, department or organisation while maintaining your main post), rotations, in-service training (training provided by or within the organisation) or mentoring/teaching colleagues. Work-based learning may also include e-learning activities such as e-modules or can be linked to more formal opportunities such as professional programmes or journal clubs. Although some of the activities may be considered informal, you still need clear reasons for pursuing them and there is still a need for their outcome to be measured.

Why would you undertake work-based learning?

Work-based learning is a good way of transferring knowledge by bridging the 'theory to practice' gap and ensuring that practice learns immediately from this new knowledge. As work-based learning activities are usually provided on an in-house basis, they are cost-effective (Lloyd et al. 2014) and provide an excellent way for staff in the organisation to share their skills and experience while developing their own skills further. For example, shadowing a colleague can help to broaden your own practice skills while you also share your knowledge in this area with your colleague.

How would you measure the success of your work-based learning?

As the aim of work-based learning is to improve outcomes for service users, staff and the organisation, its success needs to be measured by analysing changes in these areas. For example, if you have been working to develop your clinical skills in one specific area, has your intervention had a positive impact for your service users in terms of performance, speed of recovery or length of stay? It is sometimes difficult to measure this impact accurately without a purposely designed research project. However, you may only require presentation of case studies, and/or positive feedback from your supervisor, colleagues, service users and/or carers, as evidence to satisfy re-registration requirements. You may subsequently decide that a specifically designed research project is required (see 'Formal activities' above).

How does work-based learning count as CPD?

As illustrated above, and as with all CPD activities, it is what you go on to do with what you have learnt, in order to improve your practice and service delivery and how this benefits your service users, that provides you with evidence of your learning to meet the HCPC standards (HCPC 2012a, 2012c). For further information about work-based learning, see Alsop (2013), Chapter 7.

Journal clubs

Journal clubs can be profession-specific or interprofessional and can be used to discuss the evidence surrounding a great range of subjects. They usually involve a group of people coming together to discuss the merits and limitations of a particular journal article. Alternatively, each person presents evidence from a range of articles on a specific subject. It is also possible to participate in free online journal clubs (see the section on social media in Chapter 5). There is no single way to run a journal club but there are a few important points to bear in mind, whichever format is chosen:

- You should agree on the ground rules and guidelines before the first meeting to ensure that all participants understand their responsibilities in terms of what they should read or search for and the time allowed.
- All evidence presented should be critiqued, preferably using a critique tool such as CASP (Critical Appraisal Skills Programme 2015).

Why should you join a journal club?

Journal clubs are an excellent way to work with others to establish an evidence base to support your practice (Waite & Keenan 2010). This can be invaluable if you are required to demonstrate that you are using the most current evidence to support your work.

How can you measure the benefit of journal clubs?

- Complete a reading record, including references and a short summary of your findings, to provide evidence that you have undertaken the reading
- Write or record a reflection to show how you will apply what you have learnt
- Complete an intervention evidence log (see Chapter 8)
- Disseminate what you have learnt to your colleagues or other professionals to demonstrate your understanding, with consideration given to the most effective way to do this (see Chapter 4).

How does being a member of a journal club count as CPD?

- It develops knowledge of the evidence base
- It develops skills of critique
- It can enable the formation of guidelines for practice to support an intervention.

Professional or external activities

In this context, professional or external activities can be any of the following:

- Activities that relate specifically to your own profession, such as being a placement educator or an active member of a special interest group, or undertaking work for your professional body
- External activities that require you to be working in your professional capacity, such as external examining, activities for a regulatory body (e.g. HCPC re-approvals) or membership of a university or health/social care related committee, or acting as an expert witness
- Specific roles where a prerequisite is for you to be a qualified professional in a specific field; you may or may not be required to undertake additional focused training (e.g. to become an approved mental health practitioner or non-medical prescriber)
- External activities where your professional qualification is not necessarily a prerequisite but the learning obtained contributes to your overall professional practice (e.g. volunteering for a charity or third sector organisation, or undertaking public service duties).

Why would you undertake professional/external activities?

Professional/external activities are excellent career development opportunities, as they can provide you with a helicopter view of the organisation/s for which you are working/acting in an advisory capacity. They can also help to broaden your knowledge in various areas that can be applied to influence your professional practice. Even within a special interest group, although the focus is usually on a specialist area of practice, rich learning opportunities can be provided in relation to specialist practice across a wide range of locations or professions.

How would you measure the success of your professional/external activities?

The success of your professional/external activities can be measured in a variety of ways, especially if it is cross-referenced back to your original learning objectives. If you have undertaken specific training, a certificate or qualification may be a useful measurement of success in relation to your professional activities. However, other specific measurements need to be designed around the individual activity. For example, you may set your own individual targets; or, if you are an external examiner, success could be measured through positive feedback from the institution regarding your contribution and responses to your suggestions.

How do professional/external activities count as CPD?

● They lead to improved formal report-writing skills

● They can sometimes provide specific management or leadership skills

● They provide essential networks to support professional practice, such as active participation in Heads of Service meetings

● They give you greater political and contextual awareness, which can enhance your professional practice

● They increase your awareness of new developments in knowledge, practice and technology

● They help you develop advanced professional and interprofessional communication skills

● They enhance your employability and potentially help to improve your career prospects.

Professional support

Professional support refers to the types of roles and responsibilities undertaken at your place of work. These can include:

● Supervision – a structured process implemented within the workplace to increase understanding of practice and management issues, reflect on their impact on practice and the service user and to drive evidence-based and high-quality practice. Many strategies are in place to support supervision. Although supervision as an activity does not necessarily constitute CPD, the outcomes of your formal discussions may form part of your personal and professional development.

● Mentorship – this can be either formal or informal and is designed to support the long-term professional development of an individual or group. The focus is on the facilitation of learning through a supportive environment, rather than overseeing and guiding practice (as in supervision).

● Coaching – usually provided by an external facilitator. Coaching enables people to identify their learning needs in relation to their role or future aspirations, and provide strategies to enable them to analyse and achieve their learning objectives.

● Preceptorship (or equivalent) – a process for new practitioners to guide, facilitate and measure development of professional skills during the formative stages of their careers (DH 2010).

These roles may or may not be undertaken with people from your own profession. (See also Chapter 7 for more in-depth information on the above professional support activities.)

Why would you undertake professional support?

In the health sector, supervision is a requirement of clinical governance, and preceptorship has been introduced as a requirement within Agenda for Change. Similar approaches are in use across social care – for example, Assessed and Supported Year in Employment (ASYE) for social workers. Although mentorship and coaching are not mandatory, all these activities have similar benefits, which are to promote professional practice and therefore increase provision of high-quality care for all service users.

How would you measure the success of professional support?

● Through its impact on job satisfaction, confidence and competence in the role, and through staff retention

● Through positive feedback from service users

● Through confirmed achievement of objectives set through supervision, appraisal and professional development review processes.

How does professional support count as CPD?

All the above activities facilitate CPD but, in order to count *as CPD*, it is important that you – as an individual – fully engage with each process. On their own, they have little or no impact on your professional development.

These activities can help you:

● Develop greater confidence and ability in your professional role

● Develop your understanding of professional issues and their application

● Gain opportunities to develop skills in reflection

● Find a forum for the sharing of good practice

● Access opportunities to consider and test out strategies to improve practice

● Develop your ability to work with others by making links between knowledge and personal experience.

Training

Training consists of CPD activities such as courses, attending and/or presenting at conferences (see Chapter 4) and workshops or facilitating/chairing these events. These are usually short scheduled activities, for which you may need to place a formal application, and seek permission for funding and/or time to attend from your manager. They are often themed events, with presenters who are considered experts in their fields – for example, your professional body peer-reviewed annual conference, specialist skill or assessment training or a specific CPD workshop. Training can also include courses that provide accreditation for taking students on practice or clinical placements. These events are often advertised as 'meeting CPD requirements' or 'CPD accredited' (for instance, courses where a CPD certificate is awarded for attending and/or points may be attached).

Although mandatory training should be recorded, it does not usually count as CPD activity in itself, as it is enforced training to ensure safe practice, rather than training selected to advance your professional development. As with other training, just because you have undertaken mandatory training, it does not necessarily mean you have addressed any more than an 'Activity' in the TRAMm stations. However, it is possible to learn something in mandatory training that you later transfer to your practice. Having transferred it to your practice, it may then make a positive difference to your service users – for example, in the form of new assessments or techniques.

Why would you undertake training?

You might decide to undertake training because you have:

- Identified a learning need with your manager during a supervision or annual review
- Identified a learning need independently – for your career development or in an area of work you would like to move into, or because you know your organisation is keen to promote and engage with an area of practice.

Most people will opt to attend formal training because they wish to update themselves on current developments – for example, the latest evidence-based practice across their profession from within the UK and further afield. They may also wish to develop their knowledge and skills in a specialist area of practice, where there is no expertise within their organisation.

Formal training events enable you to build links and professional networks outside your organisation; they also offer opportunities to promote your own best practice and research. Some people attend these events to restore their faith in their profession and to re-motivate themselves. Others may never have attended a formal event but have perhaps been inspired to attend by colleagues. Some have attended but feel they have not benefited; this may be because they have not prepared or made the most of opportunities that were available (see Chapter 1, case study, p. 8).

In order to attend a formal training event, you may need to negotiate funding with your manager. If this is the case, it is important to ensure that you have explicitly identified a learning need in your annual review, appraisal or supervision (see Chapters 7 and 8). Once you have identified an appropriate formal training opportunity, you need to do your homework and thoroughly investigate the details of the programme, presenters and full potential costs – including travel, accommodation, subsistence and fees.

You can present your evidence of identified learning needs using TRAMmCPD through supervision or review/appraisal:

- Clearly demonstrate why and how your chosen formal training event will meet your objectives
- Refer to any evidence-based practice that is available to support the need for your attendance – for example, a new treatment where there is currently no internal skill base
- Look at professional body websites where there maybe templates available for letters to apply for funding and/or present a business case for why you should be allowed to attend
- Demonstrate how your attendance will benefit your organisation and how you will disseminate the information on your return
- Consider alternative funding sources so that your employer may only need to give you study leave (for instance, charities, academies, companies, part self-funding).

How do you measure the effectiveness of formal training?

The effectiveness of formal training can be measured in many and varied ways, depending upon the nature and purpose of the event. (For details, see Chapter 8.)

How to get the most out of conferences

Before the conference:

- Obtain a copy of the conference programme at the earliest opportunity, ideally before the event itself so that you have time to study it in depth; programmes can initially appear very complicated so ask someone who has attended previously for their assistance.
- Identify and highlight the most appropriate events in the conference programme, making notes about their location within the venue, particularly if you will need to move swiftly between sessions.

During the conference:

- If you use social media and decide to communicate during sessions, study the conference social media guidelines, and ensure you adhere to your professional code of conduct. Use the agreed conference code (e.g. Twitter #).
- Download any conference tools, such as apps, online timetables or abstracts.
- To make the best use of your time, firstly identify your priorities, check for clashes and ensure you have booked your place in any sessions where this is required.
- Allow time to view posters and exhibitors' stands.
- Make time to network with others – you will be surprised how much you can gain from this.
- Make notes, doodles and reflections, as you think of them.

After the conference:

- Complete your TRAMm Tracker with brief details of your attendance.
- Initiate a TRAMm Trail – include details of the sessions you attended, what you learnt and how you will use the information and contacts to benefit your organisation and service users.

- Consider how you will disseminate what you have learnt to your colleagues and manager.
- Think about how you will apply what you learnt at the conference to benefit your service users.
- At your next supervision, discuss using TRAMm Tracker and TRAMm Trail to summarise the benefits of your attendance and your future plans.

How does this type of training count as CPD?

Training provided through courses, workshops and conferences is one of the most commonly considered activities for CPD because people believe that these activities can provide quick, easily accessible evidence, with supporting CPD certificates or credit points. However, in order to meet the HCPC standards, it is essential to include evidence showing how the training has impacted on your practice and improved outcomes for service users and carers. This should be the focus of your subsequent reflections and your plans for your future learning needs, and can be recorded on your TRAMm Tracker and TRAMm Trail.

How to get the most out of courses and workshops

The principles are very similar to those that apply when attending a conference (see above) but there may be some differences.

Before the course or workshop:

- Complete any required pre-course reading or work (e.g. pre-course e-module)
- Undertake background reading if no prerequisite work or prior knowledge of the subject has been specified
- Consider your own expectations and objectives for attending to ensure that these are addressed
- Check whether there are any clothing or other special requirements for the day
- Find out whether lunch and refreshments are provided.

After the course or workshop:

- Complete your TRAMm Tracker, including the title of the training event and the date
- For the most significant sessions, initiate a TRAMm Trail, including what you attended, what you learnt and how you will use the information and contacts to benefit your organisation and service users
- Consider how you will disseminate what you learnt to your colleagues and manager.
- Think about how you will apply what you have learnt to benefit your service users.

Informal support

CPD often starts with an activity, and informal support can often be the first in a series of CPD activities relating to a specific area of skill or knowledge development. Informal support does not always begin as an explicit CPD activity; instead you may find yourself in a situation where you suddenly recognise there are learning opportunities at your disposal.

Informal support can be received or provided in a number of ways and can include, for example, peer group support, informal mentorship, and ad hoc discussion forums (such as discussions in the staff room or office). Journal clubs (see p. 84) may also fit in this category if they are locally organised within a department, although they can also be a more formal arrangement if they are part of larger interprofessional events. Informal support may advance your learning or provide the impetus for further learning to occur. An example might be a scenario in a staff room, where a colleague shares informally her experience of a recent course where she learnt about a new intervention. You may end up discussing how the intervention can be useful with your specific service user group, or it may just provide an incentive to find out more and attend a course yourself. Either way, you may be developing your professional knowledge and understanding of a specific area.

Why would you undertake informal support?

Informal support can usually be accessed a lot more quickly than more formal support mechanisms and is often therefore more timely for you and your service user in relation to support or intervention required. However, with these informal activities, it is important to be clear on how they have contributed to your CPD, rather than just being 'normal' work activities.

For example, in the above scenario in the staff room, if you just listen to your colleague and ask a few questions about what she is discussing with others, this is probably just a normal workplace activity involving sharing of information. However, if you use this discussion as a springboard to further your interest and you undertake further research, take your ideas to supervision and undertake further related learning activities in order to apply this to your service user group, then this may have contributed considerably to your CPD. This process can be usefully reflected and recorded on a TRAMm Trail.

How would you measure the success of informal support?

It is often more difficult to measure the success of informal support, although it can be linked to client outcome if it is a very clear and specific activity.

How does informal support count as CPD?

Informal support does not, in and of itself, count as CPD but, depending on the informal support received or provided, it can contribute to CPD in various ways. It is therefore important to remind yourself of the HCPC definition and standards required of CPD (as outlined in Chapter 1) in order to recognise CPD opportunities as they are presented. Informal support may:

- Count as the first in a series of activities designed to further your knowledge and skills
- Initiate or inform reflection on a specific situation or service user.

Social media

Social media uses online technology to enable and encourage social interactions and is becoming increasing popular as the quickest and most cost-effective way to keep up to date with legislation and research and as an effective method of networking with like-minded people, both professionals and service users, locally and internationally. Social media can also be used to promote your skills or service and disseminate or discuss good practice.

There are many different types of social media, including apps, blogs, information collation tools, and social and business networking sites. Other types include video sharing, online communities and document sharing. Discussion forums, online chats and online journal clubs are becoming increasingly popular ways of using social networking sites to participate in CPD. These can help to encourage intra-professional and interprofessional communication via profession-specific and CPD-specific groups on popular social networking sites. Here you are able to pose questions to the wider community, follow conference sessions and make comments. These suggestions are by no means exhaustive; as technology advances, the methods and sites available are constantly changing and evolving.

Whichever type of online networking you use, it is important to adhere to the social media guidelines provided by the HCPC (HCPC 2015b), your professional body or organisation/employer. It is also imperative that you are fully aware of your code of ethics and professional conduct, as this applies to *all* your online interactions across all platforms, whether professional or social. It is particularly vital to maintain service user/colleague confidentiality at all times in all interactions.

Links to (or hard copies of) your social media interactions or collations may contribute to your CPD, as long as they help provide evidence of how you have met the HCPC standards for CPD (see Chapters 4 and 5).

Why would you use social media?

There are many reasons why you might wish to engage with aspects of social media, including:

- It is free to use so it is very cost effective – there is no charge to use most sites, and no printing or postal costs
- It provides networking opportunities and allows the promotion of research, products, organisations and professional body activities
- It provides professional support if you work in an isolated area or you are receiving supervision from a different profession
- It enhances communication and allows you to engage with a wider audience, which can include professionals, commissioners, service users and carers
- Responses can be instant so you can obtain swift answers to queries or ideas from others that you had not considered.

Despite all the benefits it is important to remember that, to some, the vast array of social media activities available can appear daunting and overwhelming. There can be a fear of open criticism and abuse and a concern about getting things wrong, especially as interactions are viewed by so many people.

If you are a novice user of social media and would like to get involved, talk to colleagues to see what they are using and stick to your own professional sites. You do not always have to participate; you can 'lurk' to observe what is going on and to gain an understanding of how people interact.

How can you measure the success of your use of social media?

Complete your TRAMm Tracker, including dates with relevant links

- For your most significant sessions and interactions, initiate a TRAMm Trail – include what you contributed to, and where to access the information in the future
- Develop an understanding of, and use, different media to save or record useful information
- Keep a record of what you learnt and how you will use what you have learnt to benefit your practice, organisation and/or service users
- Can you disseminate what you have learnt to your colleagues or manager? How will you do this?
- Write or record a reflection to show how you will apply what you have learnt.

How does social media interaction count as CPD?

- It helps you build wider professional networks
- It provides often immediate, up-to-date knowledge of new developments
- It allows participation in online journal clubs to critically evaluate evidence and aspects of practice
- It provides a forum to discuss and debate current issues related to practice and to consider your own position in relation to these, which may encourage you to make positive changes to your practice
- It can also provide a running record of evidence of your participation in CPD activities.

Self-directed learning

Self-directed learning is anything that is undertaken on an individual and informal basis that helps to expand learning or knowledge. This can involve activities such as e-learning, including the use of multimedia technology for learning and informal research, reading journal articles and speaking to other professionals and agencies. According to Knowles (1975, p. 18), 'In its broadest meaning, "self-directed learning" describes a process by which individuals take the initiative, with or without the assistance of others, in diagnosing their learning needs, formulating learning goals, identifying human and material resources for learning, choosing and implementing appropriate learning strategies, and evaluating learning outcomes.' (For more details, see Chapter 2.)

Why would you undertake self-directed learning?

Self-directed learning can be a quick and easy way to establish knowledge, as it relies upon no one else and can usually be easily resourced. Within the introduction to TRAMmCPD, we have established that CPD is a personal and individual journey. In applying the process of self-directed learning (Knowles 1975), you as the individual would decide what you need to learn, the resources and strategies you need to support this learning, and how you will know if you have been successful.

How would you measure the success of your self-directed learning?

The success of self-directed learning can be measured in a variety of ways, but will particularly be cross-referenced back to the original objectives of learning. In the example above, the success can be measured in the benefit afforded to the service user.

How does self-directed learning count as CPD?

● Extended knowledge is carried forward into future working practices

● It may put you in a position to offer advice to others in similar situations in future

● It helps you develop useful professional networks for future learning opportunities

● It gives you an opportunity to gain knowledge of the roles of other professional colleagues.

Reflection

As detailed in Chapter 5, reflection is a complex process of analysis, critical awareness and self-evaluation that results in a change of practice. Reflection is more effectively undertaken verbally, or via a written record, following a model, as this facilitates consideration of all issues surrounding the topic, including those that may be challenging (such as personal values and beliefs and their impact on what you are trying to achieve).

However, reflection can be undertaken as an internal conversation on an informal and regular basis, using more formal verbal and written reflections to address areas where greater understanding and awareness is required. Models and methods of reflection are covered in more depth in Chapter 5 ('Record'). Moon (2004a, 2004b) contain some useful resources to enable you to reflect effectively.

Why would you undertake reflection?

Reflection is undertaken to allow practitioners to attempt to make sense of what they have done, or consider outcomes and critical events. The main aim is to help consolidate learning and develop practice.

How would you measure the success of your reflections?

● Reflection enables you to clearly document and express antecedents, behaviours and consequences contributing to an event or situation

● Your reflection shows that you have made a positive change to your practice, which impacts on your service users; its success can then be measured through service user feedback, observation or outcome measure

● If you initiate a TRAMm Tracker event, you can record the fact that reflection has been undertaken

● You can also measure its success according to how clearly you can disseminate what you have learnt to others.

How does reflection count as CPD?

● Reflective models provide a vehicle through which you can consider and adapt your professional practice

● Written reflections can also provide evidence of your clinical reasoning and how you have used newly gained knowledge and skills to influence your practice and benefit service users.

Working in emerging or non-traditional roles or taking a career break

This chapter has only illustrated a few of the most common forms of CPD activity to show the possible range, but there are a great many other activities that could be included. If you are in a non-traditional, emerging role or you are taking a career break, you need to be a little more creative in how you match your CPD activities to the HCPC Standards for Proficiency and CPD. For most this is possible, although the complexity of this creative challenge varies depending on your particular professional group.

Emerging or non-traditional roles are those where you may be working using some or all of your professional skills but not necessarily explicitly (Treseder 2012) – for example, working as a care home manager or in a women's refuge. You could be on a career break but working part-time as a sports coach, running a playgroup or working in a cafe. In each of these cases, it is important to consider the demands of the role and how the skills you are using or developing link to those required for your profession. So, for example, if you are running a playgroup you could be developing your skills of leadership, communicating with children or learning about the value of play. In contrast, if you are in a women's refuge, you may be learning more about working with people who have suffered significant psychological or physical abuse or about managing conflict.

To maintain or renew your registration in such circumstances, you will still need to consider how to evidence your CPD. It is important to find an approach that suits you, decide how and what you will measure, and seek the support of a mentor from your profession to act as a sounding board and give you guidance (see Chapter 7). Remember that it is always possible to keep learning and developing so do not give up purely because you are no longer working in an explicitly professional role.

Case study: Sally undertakes a mixture of activities

Sally is an occupational therapist who attended a two-day conference, where she participated in a TRAMmCPD workshop. Following this, she decided she needed to become more strategic in her approach to CPD. In Chapter 2 Sally realised she should participate and engage in activities for learning to occur, and she needed to develop her reflective skills further. Sally has now started to use TRAMmCPD to frame and record her progress, and is using supervision to help identify and articulate her CPD plans. She has also begun to disseminate her learning, and record and organise her achievements in her portfolio.

Sally has recently rotated to her new post in neuro-rehabilitation. In a supervision session prior to leaving her last post, she identified some training needs and agreed to investigate suitable training opportunities.

Sally discovers that there is a three-week Bobath training programme coming up in London towards the end of her rotation period. She also sees a two-day programme run by the local special interest group, which is scheduled in three weeks' time (a formal training opportunity). She decides to put together a case to attend the two-day training. This will be at the right level and she can fund it herself if her manager will allow her to take the time off work. The course in London is very specialised and expensive. Although she would love to do something like this, she decides that it is more appropriate for her to specialise in neuro-rehabilitation at a later date. She notes the details in her TRAMm Trail plan, with a view to revisiting this in the future if applicable.

Before rotating, Sally has a quick look on the Internet to locate some credible websites, with video footage illustrating the brain and its functions, as she knows this will help her to remember things more easily (self-directed learning). These enable her to update herself on her neuro-anatomy and neuro-physiology, to understand the pathology of the conditions and the range of deficits she is likely to encounter when working with people with neurological conditions. She has also retrieved her neuroscience handouts and lecture notes from university. Using a mind map, she has formulated a summary of the core aspects, including an overview of the nervous system with components of each of the central and peripheral nervous systems. She has also printed off and labelled a diagram of the brain and spinal cord, together with a table of the core components and the functions and possible deficits relating to each one.

At each supervision, she has agreed to present one case study to demonstrate her understanding in this area (informal presentation). Her new line manager has suggested that Sally integrates the NICE guidelines, professional guidelines and National Care Pathway information in the cases she presents.

One of Sally's goals was to develop a greater understanding of the application of neuro-developmental approaches. As she is a predominantly kinaesthetic learner, she asks for an opportunity to work with her colleagues (work-based learning) who have expertise in this area by first observing, then practising the relevant techniques and therapeutic handling approaches. This, she hopes, will help her to maximise the benefit of the two-day training course she will attend in three weeks' time.

Having attended the course, Sally updates her TRAMm Tracker and Trails at regular intervals to reflect the range of activities she has undertaken. She also enters a new line on her TRAMm Tracker and a new Trail to specifically focus on the neuro-developmental approaches she has studied on the course and to show how she utilises the information in her practice. See Figures 6.1 and 6.2.

Tasks

The following tasks will encourage you to consider the activities you have already undertaken and reflect on the most significant. This will enable you to reflect upon your identified learning needs and intended outcomes.

1. Consider two of the most recent and significant activities you have undertaken (one formal, one informal) and use a reflective model (see Chapter 5) to articulate why they have been significant, what you have learned, and what you intend to change or develop in your practice as a result.

2. Think about the types of activities you currently undertake. Can you identify other types of activity that you could engage in to widen the scope of your CPD? Remember to be realistic in terms of cost, time and other resources available.

3. Think about the activities you are already undertaking that could be considered as CPD or could easily be developed further to become CPD. It may be useful to discuss this with colleagues. This exercise will be especially useful if you are working in extended scope/emerging roles or are currently taking a career break.

4. How could you apply your learning from your activities in order to develop your practice and benefit your service users?

5. Continue to update your TRAMm Tracker event and complete the relevant columns.

6. For the most significant interactions and events, initiate or revisit your TRAMm Trail – include what happened, where your evidence is stored and when you will revisit to update it. Ensure you enter dates where appropriate.

7. What do you need to consider or do next in order to meet the HCPC standards? Or which TRAMm stations do you still need to visit? Complete the Plan of Action section on your Trail/s and then detail this as SMART objectives on a learning contract.

8. Read Chapter 7 to discover more about the mechanisms for monitoring your CPD (TRAMm station 'Monitor').

TRAMm TRACKER Chapter 6: *Updated tracker* Name: Sally OT

Date	Subject	Description	Certificate	Reflection	TRAMm Trail	HCPC Standards 1	2	3	4	5	TRAMm T	R	A	M	m	Index	Notes
DD/MM/YY	Two day training course	Neuro-developmental approaches	C	R	T	1	2				T	R	A	M		2	TRAMm Trail: Stored on CPD usb. Certificate in CPD portfolio
DD/MM/YY	Self-directed Learning	Rotation into Neuro Rehabilitation		R	T	1	2	3	4		T	R	A	M			See TRAMm Trail: Rotation into Neurological Rehabilitation. Stored on CPD usb
DD/MM/YY	Preceptorship	Preceptorship completed		R		1	2	3	4		T	R	A	M	m		All documentation stored in Preceptorship file
DD/MM/YY	Conference workshop	TRAMm Model for CPD with overview of HCPC standards			T	1	2	3	4		T	R	A	M	m		TRAMmCPD TRAMm Trail initiated (Date) Trail stored on CPD usb and updated (ongoing)
DD/MM/YY	Conference	Conference Day 2	C			1	2						A			1	Attended Stroke Rehabilitation Seminar, TRAMmCPD workshop. CPD certificate of attendance stored in CPD file
DD/MM/YY	Conference	Attended 2 day conference Day 1	C			1	2						A			1	Viewed poster display, exhibitor stands, attended session: Professional use of Social Media

Figure 6.1 Sally's TRAMm Tracker. Entries in green highlight updates from previous chapter.

TRAMm Trail

Please note: The TRAMm Trail has been designed for you to plan and record in a little more depth your most significant pieces of CPD. It is not anticipated that you would complete this for every piece of your CPD, only those you feel may be useful for evidence if called by the HCPC for audit. Remember to maintain confidentiality.

TRAMm Trail Title: Chapter 6: Neuro-developmental approaches   **Date: MM/YY – MM/YY**

Tell (T)	Record (R)	Activities (A)
• Informal discussion with colleagues on Stroke Unit requesting any useful reading or information about neurodevelopmental approaches (DD/MM/YY/ - ongoing) • Supervision with new line manager to include monthly presentation of case studies	• Notes written on core principles and differences between approaches to intervention (DD/MM/YY) • Notes of questions to asked regarding NICE guidelines, Care Pathway and COT Guidance stored on usb (DD/MM/YY) • Supervision record documenting the positive verbal feedback from mentor (DD/MM/YY) • Written Reflection using Gibbs Model of Reflection (DD/MM/YY) • TRAMm Tracker updated (ongoing) • TRAMm Trail initiated (DD/MM/YY)	• Neurodevelopmental two day course (DD/MM/YY) • Viewed on-line video footage to revise neurophysiology and anatomy along with functions/deficits (DD/MM/YY) • Downloaded latest NICE Guidance and National Care Pathway regarding Stroke (DD/MM/YY) and the latest COT Guidance on Stroke (DD/MM/YY) • Revised Neurodevelopmental approaches from university handouts (DD/MM/YY) • Participated in online journal club (Title of Journal article) (DD/MM/YY) • Working alongside expert practitioner practicing techniques learnt on course(DD/MM/YY)

Monitor (M)	Measure (m)	HCPC Standards met: 1, 2, 3, 4
• Formal discussion of training in Supervision with Manager, reviewed TRAMm Tracker, Trail and reviewed aims and objectives set (DD/MM/YY) • Using expert practitioner as mentor in neuro rehabilitation to monitor skill progression (ongoing)	• Anecdotal evidence- positive verbal feedback received from Mentor highlighting good understanding of approaches and application in practice (DD/MM/YY)	**PLAN of ACTION:** • **Update TRAMm Tracker and TRAMm Trail (ongoing)** • **Update Reflection after 6 months**

Figure 6.2 Sally's TRAMm Trail: Neuro-development

7

How do you keep track of your CPD?
TRAMm Station M: MONITOR

Managers need to take a proactive role in the CPD of all their staff and to enable agreed activities to be undertaken with clearly defined outcomes and monitoring arrangements. It is also important that individuals take some responsibility for monitoring their own CPD. There are several ways of monitoring CPD, such as supervision, mentorship and reflection.

This chapter discusses the mechanisms for monitoring CPD. It explores in depth the meaning of the terms 'supervision' and 'mentorship' and considers how being a mentor or being mentored can support CPD. It also explores ways in which supervision and other strategies (such as peer review) may be used to keep track of personal and professional development.

The final part of this chapter will explore the use of the TRAMm Tracker and Trail as part of the monitoring process and this will be illustrated in the case study.

Tasks at the end of the chapter will encourage you to consider the value of mentorship and supervision and how you can maximise their potential as part of your own professional development.

What do we mean by 'Monitor'?

Reviewing the growth of knowledge, skills and attitudes is an important part of any individual's personal and professional development. The annual appraisal or performance review is often cited as the only time when personal and professional development is officially reviewed; yet, if used properly, appraisal should represent a formal measurement of progress (see Chapter 8 for further details). While formal measurement is important, it does not remove the need for regular and timely feedback on your performance, which enables you to grow steadily, or the need for informal support from someone who can help you explore your aspirations or concerns.

In the TRAMm model, 'Monitor' refers to this action of keeping track or reviewing your progress so you can alter your approach or change direction if you find what you are doing is not meeting your learning needs. If you are in a management position, it refers to the actions you take to monitor the CPD being undertaken in your team. It can involve a range of formal and informal mechanisms (such as supervision, mentorship and peer review) and is part of a 'formative' process that helps to facilitate your CPD. In this TRAMm station M (Monitor), the term 'formative' is key: whichever monitoring mechanism is adopted, it should simply provide feedback, and not be used to provide a summative measure of performance to which some kind of reward is attached (such as promotion, salary increase or qualification). Some mechanisms can be used to monitor and measure progress and, where this is the case, the distinction will be clarified.

Why is it important to monitor progress?

Monitoring and tailoring of progress enables you to identify personal and professional strengths and needs. It is also a process whereby managers can maintain an overview of their most important and expensive resource (staff) by keeping track of the strengths and development needs of their organisation. There are many occasions when an individual's personal and professional development needs may be different from those of the organisation; and it is essential to be clear about these expectations to ensure that we are monitoring development appropriately.

The value of monitoring CPD for the individual

When considering the importance of monitoring, a good analogy is the education process, which we all experience during our careers. Think back to when you were at school. You will have had classes (teaching) during your studies and exams at the end of each term or year (summative assessments) but what formative tasks and assessments did you have to support your learning? Homework, presentations and class tests were not only included for the teachers' benefit. They were also put in place to monitor your progress in understanding and ability. Doing poorly in homework or a class test did not mean that you failed the year and could not progress. It just meant that your teacher, your parents and you yourself knew where you were struggling and where further support or tuition was required to enable you to pass your exams. If you had received classroom teaching on its own, you could have wasted a whole year – and perhaps ended up failing because of problems that could have been easily addressed but were not picked up earlier through your formative work.

As health and care professionals, the same will apply during your practice or clinical placements; or, if you are a health or care student, this may be something you are already familiar with. You will have had some instruction from your placement or clinical educators but, without regular and timely monitoring and feedback, you could continue to perform badly until you discovered you had failed at the end of the placement period. This would be a waste of time, not only for you but also for your placement educators. More importantly, it could cause harm or distress to patients or service users and a significant waste of money for the service. Fortunately, it is common to get regular informal feedback, observed assessments and encouragement to reflect through more formal supervision to help you recognise your strengths and make plans to address your learning needs.

For those of you reading this who have had a less favourable experience of placement, the main reason for this may well have been poor monitoring or feedback. If you are a student and have just had a placement, or are currently on placement, it may be useful to reflect upon your experiences of monitoring and feedback. It is also important to note that monitoring and feedback is not only undertaken to identify and rectify problems. Monitoring can also be useful to highlight and further develop a person's strengths, as can be seen in the example below.

Example 7.1 Adam, the operating department practitioner

Adam is an operating department practitioner who is six months into his first post on the orthopaedic surgical team. Adam has had to learn several new skills since commencing this role. These have been highlighted as part of his preceptorship programme and he is now beginning to recognise his increase in confidence. His supervisor has helped him to understand the department processes, which he can now follow without supervision, and his communication skills in recovery have been noted as excellent by the ward manager.

Recently Adam's manager has observed that whenever students are in the department he is particularly proactive in helping to support them. They in turn seem to respond well to his teaching and he is able to explain things clearly and concisely. This strength is discussed at Adam's next supervision. When Adam admits that teaching is something he would like to do, it is agreed that he will undertake the post-registration course on supervision of students.

Monitoring is also used to check on progress in terms of career direction. Very few of us know exactly which area we wish to specialise in when we are undertaking our professional studies or when newly qualified. Instead we explore a few specialist areas via rotations or several job applications until we find an area that motivates us, as a result of a clinical interest or because we find we are good at it. Even then, we may not stay in that area – either because we specialise further or we choose to change direction. (For example, perhaps moving into management or education or promotion leads us down a different path or we retrain in a different profession.) If we review Adam in five years' time, it is possible that he will have re-evaluated his career direction and either moved to a different specialty or retrained as a theatre nurse to gain greater autonomy in surgical care. In this way, the process of monitoring and feedback helps us to pursue our career aspirations and consider opportunities, reviewing our own preferences in relation to the options available to us.

The value of monitoring CPD for the organisation

The RCN (2007) recommended that healthcare professionals received at least 45 hours per year for CPD in order to maintain competence and develop their practice to adapt to the changing needs of the service users and organisations in which they worked. Likewise, O'Sullivan (2006) highlights the value of organisations that are committed to the learning and development of their staff (see Chapter 2 on learning organisations). If they are investing substantial time and money in CPD, it follows that the organisations themselves should also want to keep a check on what their money is paying for.

In a study exploring CPD within hospital trusts, Mathers et al. (2012) found that CPD for staff often occurred in a vacuum, with no connection to the organisation's goals or the appraisal process. In cases like this, where CPD took place in isolation, Mathers et al. (2012) found that there was less likelihood of it being implemented or documented. If you are a manager of staff in any organisation, this is important information, as it suggests that your budget (in terms of CPD costs or staff time) may be being spent on something for which you will never see a return and this is not the way a good business is run. The TRAMm model emphasises these requirements in its stations, where dissemination and planning (in 'Tell') and documentation (in 'Record') are considered essential for full engagement in CPD.

It is accepted that those who are involved in the top-level overall management of the organisation will have little time or interest in what each individual is undertaking for their CPD. However, it is their role to identify the strategic direction of the organisation and they should also ensure that these goals are relayed to line managers, who will in turn reflect these within staff development plans. If you are a line manager, you will probably measure performance via objectives set as part of the appraisal process. Regardless, it is important to undertake regular monitoring so that information about your team, and how they are contributing to the organisation, can be provided when required.

As a line manager in an organisation, you could be monitoring and documenting many aspects of CPD, including:

- The range and frequency of CPD activities undertaken by those you supervise
- The number of hours each staff member has taken as CPD
- The developing range of knowledge and skills of your team
- Evidence showing how and where this CPD has been disseminated
- Information about the impact of CPD on service user outcomes
- The running costs of CPD activities undertaken
- Income generated and money saved as a direct or indirect result of staff CPD.

This list is not exhaustive but provides some guidance, following the TRAMm model, of the important CPD aspects and how they may be reviewed. Adopting the TRAMm Tracker and TRAMm Trail for all the staff you manage could help to provide a standardised record, from which data required for the above monitoring could be easily retrieved.

How do we monitor our progress and what do we need?

There are many ways to monitor progress and encourage personal and professional development. This will also provide information for organisational monitoring, as indicated previously. The following section provides an overview of some of the most common enablers of monitoring, including:

- Supervision and clinical supervision
- Preceptorship (or equivalent)
- Mentoring
- Peer review and work-based learning as monitoring
- Self-monitoring via reflection.

Supervision and clinical supervision

Supervision is a process that is designed to provide individual staff with *accountability* (facilitating safe and effective practice), *support* and *learning* (O'Neill 2004). It is a requirement of practice (Gopee 2015) and in most working environments some time is allocated to facilitate supervision, although the amount of time varies according to your employer and/or supervisor.

According to the Care Quality Commission (CQC 2013, p. 4) clinical supervision is:

'a safe and confidential environment for staff to reflect on and discuss their work and their personal and professional responses to their work. The focus is on supporting staff in their personal and professional development and in reflecting on their practice.'

In addition, the College of Occupational Therapists (2010, p. 2) states that:

'supervision involves learning through reviewing, reflecting and discussing the experiences of the workplace, confirming and building upon the positive events and exploring options for the less easy occurrences, so developing the practitioner's understanding of their work environment and broadening their range of personal and professional resources in terms of skills and knowledge.'

Taken together, these two definitions explain what supervision can (and cannot) be expected to achieve.

The CQC (2013, pp. 3–4) identifies three main types of supervision, although the terms are often used interchangeably:

1. **Managerial supervision** is carried out by a supervisor with authority and accountability for the supervisee. It provides the opportunity for staff to:

- Review their performance
- Set priorities and objectives in line with the organisation's objectives and service needs
- Identify training and development needs.

2. **Clinical supervision** provides an opportunity for staff to:

- Reflect on their practice
- Discuss individual cases in depth
- Change or modify practice and identify training and development needs.

3. **Professional supervision** (often interchangeable with clinical supervision) is sometimes used when supervision is carried out by another member of the same profession or group. This can give staff the opportunity to:

- Review professional standards
- Keep up to date with developments in their profession
- Identify professional training and development needs
- Ensure that they are working within professional codes of conduct and boundaries.

For the purposes of this chapter, the term 'supervision' is used to refer to all the above types of supervision.

Youngstrom (2009) and professional bodies, such as the College of Occupational Therapists (COT 2010) and Chartered Society of Physiotherapists (CSP 2013), acknowledge that the main aim of supervision is to achieve safe, effective and high-quality service delivery. In order for supervision to be effective, COT (2010), CSP (2013) and Strong (2009) highlight the need for it to be conducted in a safe and supportive manner. This is especially important, as evidence suggests that employees who experience an atmosphere of fear and distrust in the workplace are more likely to make mistakes and report them less frequently (Dixon-Woods 2010). This failure to report mistakes can not only stunt individual professional growth but also stifle organisational learning; and in the clinical field, it can potentially cause harm to service users.

In a study of allied health professionals, Strong et al. (2003) discovered that supervision helped to increase job satisfaction, effectiveness and reasoning, concurrently preventing stress and burnout, two factors that have been associated with poor patient safety (Schaufeli & Bakker 2004). Strong et al. (2009) also identified the benefits of supervision in terms of the organisation; staff develop greater understanding of the culture and practice of the organisation and a stronger sense of organisational identity. This in turn assists both recruitment and retention.

The COT (2010) highlights the importance of considering context and personal preference in order to decide on the most appropriate supervision style and format. Thus, for example in the NHS where supervision is an accepted part of practice, it is likely to follow a clinical supervision style (CQC 2013) on a one-to-one basis. In a specialist unit, where there is a small expert team, they may prefer the option of group supervision, which may also be the preferred format when teams are dealing with complex cases – as in social care. Peer supervision, or long-arm supervision, may be the style of choice when a professional is working in professional isolation or in a non-traditional or role-emerging setting. Advances in the use of technology have also seen the emergence of e-supervision, whereby meetings can take place via Skype, video-conference or E-discussion.

Whichever supervision style is selected, the core principles remain the same and are reflected in many books, articles and professional body statements. These principles are most effectively summarised by the Chartered Society of Physiotherapy (CSP 2013, p. 1).

According to the CSP (2013), clinical supervision should:

1. Support and enhance practice for the benefit of patients and service users

2. Develop skills in reflection to narrow the gap between theory and practice (see Chapter 5)

3. Involve a supervisor and practitioner, or group of practitioners, reflecting on and critically evaluating practice

4. Be distinct from formal line management supervision and appraisal (see Chapter 8)

5. Be planned, systematic and conducted within agreed boundaries

6. Be explicit about the public and confidential elements of the process

7. Facilitate clear and unambiguous communication, conducted in an atmosphere of beneficence (keeping the welfare of the supervisee at the centre of the process)

8. Define an outcomes-based action plan that can be more broadly developed to assist the practitioner's professional development through the appraisal process (see Chapter 2)

9. Be evaluated against set standards, from the time it is initially developed and implemented.

The clinical supervision process should:

1. Involve all individuals in the service, be signed up to by staff, and supported and resourced by management

2. Be developed in partnership with managers and practitioners

3. Be supported by appropriate resources (including time, training and replacement staff)

4. Facilitate practitioner access to their chosen model of supervision, as appropriate

5. Support a local system for supervisors to further develop their skills in facilitation

6. Be developed in parallel with collating a portfolio of learning, so that the practitioner is supported to develop and demonstrate skills of reflection and evidencing learning from experience (see Chapter 5).

As a supervisee, it is important to plan for your sessions and record a summary, together with a list of actions to be undertaken following the supervision. There are various formats for recording supervision; in TRAMmCPD, the TRAMm Tracker and Trail can help to guide both you and the session itself (see Chapter 5).

Finally, if you are acting as a supervisor, it is important to allow time to undertake the supervision and keep the issues expressed by the supervisee confidential, no matter how insignificant you may think they are. You must also access appropriate training for the role. It may only be a short course but it will certainly help to clarify your role and delineate responsibilities between yourself and the supervisee.

Mentorship and the role of the mentor

Across the healthcare professions, the term 'mentoring' is used in a variety of ways. In TRAMmCPD, mentoring is traditionally defined as a process to 'support and encourage people to manage their own learning in order that they may maximise their potential, develop their skills, improve their performance and become the person they want to be' (Parsloe 2008, p. 1).

Mentoring differs from supervision in several ways. The mentor and mentee have a very different type of relationship from a supervisor and supervisee. Although the mentor is usually more senior or experienced than the mentee, the mentor tends to adopt more of a friend or 'buddy' status. The mentor is also usually from a similar field or has similar experiences to the mentee. Ideally, the mentor should be selected by the mentee, as it is important for the mentee to have someone they both respect and trust.

The role of the mentor is to advise or support, rather than to oversee performance or direct work in accordance with organisational strategy. During mentorship sessions, the focus is on the mentee and their personal and professional development over the long term. During supervision, in contrast, the focus is usually on practice and how the individual is performing in the work context, usually taking more of a short-term view. Both have a role in ensuring that the mentee understands and engages in evidence-based practice (Gopee 2015).

Mentorship sessions should ideally be directed by the needs of the mentee, with the mentee setting and leading the agenda; whereas supervision is often guided by the structure adopted in the workplace and may focus more on requirements from practice. Whereas a supervisor explores performance and practice issues, a mentor's role is to develop confidence and self-belief by asking questions and challenging thoughts and perceptions. Mentoring provides an opportunity for the mentee to explore ideas in confidence, become more self-aware and scrutinise themselves along with any issues, aspirations and potential opportunities.

Records of both supervision and mentorship are of course confidential. However, meetings with a mentor should remain strictly confidential at all times, whereas communications during supervision can be used to inform professional development and help deal with performance issues should they arise. It is therefore no surprise that the mentor and mentee can discuss any issues at all (whether personal or professional), whereas supervision generally tends to focus on work-related issues.

If you do not currently have a mentor, it is well worth considering finding one. Mentors can provide invaluable support throughout your career. They can help you think through different ways of tackling difficult situations. You can also use mentoring sessions to air concerns about your own performance or relationships at work, without fear of reprisal. Because the mentoring relationship can continue over a period of time, sessions can be invaluable as a means to facilitate self-monitoring of values, attitudes and self-image; these are issues that are difficult to reflect upon without someone to challenge you in a mutually trusting relationship.

If you feel you have the required skills and experience, becoming a mentor is also an excellent professional development opportunity and could be considered as one of your CPD activities.

Preceptorship and monitoring

Agenda for Change (DoH 2004) was a major change for all staff in the NHS. At the same time, preceptorship was introduced as a process to support newly qualified staff and facilitate CPD through their first 6–12 months. In preceptorship, successful progress through individual professional development plans, linked to the Knowledge and Skills Framework (KSF), leads to incremental advance. This is similar to ASYE for social workers (Skills for Care 2012) or probation in other organisations.

The Department of Health (DH 2010, p. 11) defines preceptorship as:

> 'A period of structured transition for the newly registered practitioner during which he or she will be supported by a preceptor, to develop their confidence as an autonomous professional, define skills, values and behaviours and to continue on their journey of lifelong learning.'

Preceptorship is one of the more formal monitoring mechanisms, in which the final outcome may be considered a form of measurement of CPD, like appraisal (see Chapter 8). However, the process allows for self-monitoring and monitoring of professional development by a superior.

The DH (2010) identifies three contributors to the preceptorship process: the preceptee, the preceptor and the employer, each of which have their respective responsibilities to ensure the process runs effectively. The employer ensures compliance with the KSF and has a responsibility to allow time for the preceptee and preceptor to meet and for professional development. The preceptor has the role of facilitating the professional development of the preceptee and providing timely and documented feedback; while the preceptee must follow the programme and take responsibility for their own learning.

There is no set format for a preceptorship programme but it is expected that it will involve theoretical, practical and attitudinal development. Like CPD, preceptorship learning can occur through a range of activities but the DH (2010) recommends that there should be approximately 4–6 days allocated for theoretical learning and around 18 hours for learning such as reflection and practice development. The exact process is usually determined by the individual organisation to ensure equity for all new staff.

There are many benefits of preceptorship for all parties (including service users) but the main advantages are that quality of care is enhanced for the service user; the employee feels valued and has job satisfaction, with increased confidence and competence in the role (Jamieson et al. 2012); and the preceptor invests in their own professional development by developing new skills.

Self-monitoring via reflection

In Chapter 5 we explored the process of reflection and a range of models to assist with it. Reflection is an excellent way to facilitate self-monitoring, particularly in relation to those aspects that are more difficult to measure, such as confidence, attitudes and values (Constable 2013).

In order to use reflection in monitoring your CPD, it is useful to undertake a reflection before you start an element of CPD – for example, at the beginning of a course or at the start of a new job or rotation. One reflection on its own can help monitor a shift in your knowledge, skills or attitudes but comparing one reflection with another can explicitly evidence a change over a period of time.

Peer review and monitoring

Peer review is appraisal of work by someone with similar competence in order to drive up quality and provide credibility. Peer review sits on the dividing line between monitoring (formative assessment to monitor progress and provide feedback) and measurement (summative assessment leading to a reward, award or outcome, depending upon its context). In this chapter we will discuss the purpose of peer review in monitoring and it will then be revisited in Chapter 8 in relation to measuring CPD.

When used for monitoring purposes, peer review is usually seen in the workplace and is often referred to as peer review in a given context – for instance, peer review of teaching or peer review of practice. In peer review of teaching, a fellow colleague will be responsible for evaluating your performance in a particular teaching situation and will provide constructive feedback. This feedback is usually kept confidential between the reviewee and reviewer, but the reviewee may choose to share the feedback in supervision or appraisal to help identify future learning needs for CPD.

Using TRAMmCPD to help you with the monitoring process

TRAMmCPD tools can help you to record and monitor your progress in various areas. The TRAMm Tracker will help you to monitor how you are meeting the HCPC standards for CPD (HCPC 2012c) and will encourage dialogue around your full engagement with the CPD process via the TRAMm stations. It will highlight deficits or omissions in certain areas and, when used with the TRAMm model, can show you how to work on those areas (see Chapter 5 for more detail on using this in practice).

The TRAMm Trail will allow you to map in greater depth your activities and ideas for some of the more complex cases that you may wish to discuss during the supervision process, and help you keep track of your progress on visiting the TRAMm stations. It also provides you with a box in which to insert your plans, to keep them readily available for monitoring purposes and for further development.

Those using the Trail have often asked us why there is a lack of information under the 'Monitoring' heading. Our answer is that it is very possible that you are struggling to complete the 'Monitor' station, as there is no monitoring currently taking place for this particular piece of CPD. You can now identify this as a gap in your learning and consciously decide to ensure that you include monitoring in future. If you decide that monitoring has been taking place, ask yourself the following questions:

- Before you started undertaking this aspect of CPD, had you made a plan of what you wanted to achieve? Was this documented or was it a thought or reflective process? It is very difficult to monitor something when you have no idea what you are monitoring.

- Were you supervised or mentored by anyone, in a formal or informal way? If not why not? Would this be a point to consider for your future Plan of Action? It is very difficult to undertake monitoring if you have no time, person or strategy to help with this.

- If you were supervised or mentored, did you find this useful? Were you able to identify points for your future development and what exactly helped you to do so? What evidence do you have of this? This evidence can be recorded as monitoring.

- Did you monitor your own progress? Did you identify new learning that you achieved as your experience progressed? Or did this lead to identifying areas where you needed to develop in the future? If you did, exactly how? If it is not clear, perhaps you should make your thoughts more explicit by undertaking a reflection to provide evidence of your monitoring. For example, you may have had some difficult discussions with a patient and family and needed to think about how you were going to approach this in the most appropriate and sensitive manner. This is about being aware of or monitoring your own limitations or gaps in knowledge and what to do about this. It is this type of thinking that may have led to your informal supervision or setting the agenda for more formal supervision.

As a supervisor, you can also use the TRAMm Tracker and Trail to structure and record supervision sessions for each individual you supervise. This ensures that you ask the same of each individual, while allowing for flexibility to reflect their particular approach to CPD.

As a manager, you could use the tools to structure the CPD for all your staff, providing a consistent mechanism for gathering the data you require in order to monitor CPD across your team or department. During the pilot stage of TRAMmCPD, several departments adopted this approach to provide a framework for their team and guide their strategy for monitoring and measuring CPD.

Case study: Sally begins to engage in the monitoring of her progress

Sally is an occupational therapist. She attended a conference, where she participated in a TRAMmCPD workshop, following which she decided she needed to become more strategic in her approach to CPD. In Chapters 2–4, Sally started to engage in CPD activities and began to disseminate the results of her

CPD, while developing her reflective skills. In Chapters 5 and 6, after rotating into a neuro-rehabilitation post, Sally learnt to use TRAMmCPD to record her progress and activities, using the Tracker and Trail, and apply her learning in practice.

Sally is now five months into her new rotation and is conscious that she has two months left before she moves into her next post in rheumatology. She is not looking forward to leaving, as she is enjoying her time in neuro-rehabilitation. She decides that now is a good time to discuss planning for both the forthcoming rotation and her future career pathway. She is concerned about sounding as if she is complaining to her supervisor so she decides to meet for coffee to talk to her friend, Joe, a psychologist who has also been acting as her mentor over the last six months.

Joe agrees that it is important for Sally to begin to plan her career development and to use her next supervision to discuss her concerns about her forthcoming rotation and how to address this. Together they explore how Sally can do this in a constructive way. Joe advises Sally to carefully consider her aspirations for the next couple of years and says he is happy to have another chat before Sally presents her thoughts in supervision. Sally uses the following week to think about what Joe has said. She undertakes a SWOT analysis to consider her current situation, including her strengths and needs but also looking at the potential opportunities available to her (Table 7.1). Sally emails a copy of her SWOT analysis to Joe and arranges to talk further on the telephone in a few days' time.

Joe and Sally decide that Sally's proposal to her supervisor will be for her to continue into her new rotation post but also discuss ways in which she can maintain her clinical interest in neuro-rehabilitation. At the same time, she would like to develop her management and leadership skills to place herself in a good position to apply for any neuro-rehabilitation Band 6 positions in the future.

Sally decides to update her Tracker with a new entry, entitled 'Career development planning'. She initiates a new TRAMm Trail, which she will update regularly over the next 12 months or until she secures a Band 6 position.

Sally has her weekly meeting with her supervisor to discuss her caseload; they have been monitoring the progress of Sally's work with a patient with complex problems. Sally is concerned that the consultant has requested an assessment of the patient's driving skills even though she feels that this is inappropriate at this stage of the patient's rehabilitation. With her supervisor, Sally agrees that the process of driving skills is a further learning need and makes a plan to address it. She documents her progress on a new TRAMm Trail. Although this is theoretically part of her normal working practice, she believes that it also contributes to her CPD, as she has limited understanding in this area. They also discuss the limited use of Gibbs as a reflective model, now that Sally is clearly beginning to reflect on a regular basis. Sally suggests that should explore other models that may help her to reflect in greater depth, such as Fish and Twinn (1997) or Rodgers (2002).

During this meeting, Sally decides to approach her supervisor with her proposals regarding her future career development. Her supervisor states that she is impressed with how Sally has prepared her case and highlights Sally's professional progress over the last 12 months, confirming her support of Sally's plans. They agree that, within the next two months, Sally should set some new goals that reflect her ambitions and outline a plan for how these can be met. As part of this development plan, Sally and her manager discuss the possibility that Sally can continue with development of a driving pathway that she has just commenced for people with neurological deficits. Her current line manager agrees to confirm this with her future new line manager in rheumatology. Sally documents this plan on her supervision record and in her new TRAMm Trail (see Figures 7.1 and 7.2).

Table 7.1 SWOT Analysis: Sally and her profile for promotion

Strengths: Internal driving forces	**Weaknesses:** Internal restraining forces
• Six months' experience and an interest in neuro-rehabilitation • Member of local neuro special interest group • Has undertaken a recent two-day course on neuro-developmental approaches • Well-organised and current CPD portfolio • Clear strategic career development plan.	• Lacks motivation for future rheumatology rotation as this is not an area of interest and does not fit with future career plans • No management experience in relation to change, staff or finance • No Masters degree or M level study to date.
Opportunities: External driving forces	**Threats:** External restraining forces
• Local active neuro special interest group offering contribution to funding for neuro-related courses • Bobath course runs annually • In-house leadership course available on annual basis; currently recruiting for start in six months' time • New financial year starts in four weeks and funding requests are invited for CPD • Accredited placement educators' course is run at the local university, which can be undertaken as an M level module • Rheumatology department, which regularly takes students – opportunity to develop supervision skills.	• Limited promotion opportunities and high competition in the local region • Band 6 positions now requesting management experience as desirable • Band 7 posts requiring Masters level study in addition to essential management skills • High level of competition for CPD funding within the organisation.

Tasks

The following tasks are designed to facilitate your thinking around the issue of monitoring and how you will apply it to yourself. They will also encourage you to think about your own role as a mentor and how CPD can enable you to undertake the role successfully:

1. Visit your own professional body website and see if they have current guidance on any of the aspects mentioned in this chapter, such as briefings on supervision, mentorship or preceptorship. Pay particular attention to your responsibilities in whichever role you are undertaking. For instance, in the role of supervisee or supervisor, what is expected of you?

2. If you are about to start your first post or about to become a preceptor for the first time, read the preceptorship framework (DH 2010), paying particular attention to your roles and responsibilities and what you should expect from others.

3. Think about how you currently monitor your own progress. Ask yourself the following: Do I monitor how I am progressing and if so how? Are there things/tools/people I could use to assist me?

4. Take time to write a reflection on your most recent experience of monitoring and feedback at your workplace; or, if you are a student, on your most recent placement. Place this reflection in your portfolio.

5. If you do not have an official mentor, consider those people who you believe could help you in this way. Then make contact with one of them to see if they would be prepared to act as your mentor.

6. If you already have a mentor, reflect upon whether you are using them appropriately. Are there ways in which the relationship could work more effectively to support your personal and professional development?

7. Consider what monitoring roles you could undertake, such as mentor or placement educator. What are your own strengths and learning needs in this area and what opportunities are available to help you to develop your role? Undertake a SWOT analysis entitled 'Me as a monitor' to help you to summarise all this.

8. Continue to develop your portfolio and add to your TRAMm Tracker and Trails.

9. Read Chapter 8 to discover more about measuring your CPD (TRAMm station 'measure').

TRAMm TRACKER Chapter 7: *Updated tracker*

Name: Sally OT

Date	Subject	Description	Certificate	Reflection	TRAMm Trail	HCPC Standards					TRAMm					Index	Notes
						1	2	3	4	5	T	R	A	M	m		
DD/MM/YY	Planning	Career development planning with mentor and supervisor	☐	☐	T	1	2	☐	☐	☐	T	R	☐	M	☐		TRAMm Trail: Stored on CPD usb. Certificate in CPD portfolio
DD/MM/YY	Two day training course	Neuro-developmental approaches	C	R	T	1	2	3	4	☐	T	R	☐	M	m	2	TRAMm Trail: Stored on CPD usb. Certificate in CPD portfolio
DD/MM/YY	Self-directed Learning	Rotation into Neurological Rehabilitation	☐	R	T	1	2	3	☐	☐	T	R	A	M	☐		See TRAMm Trail: Rotation into Neurological Rehabilitation. Stored on CPD usb
DD/MM/YY	Preceptorship	Preceptorship completed	☐	☐	☐	1	2	3	4	☐	T	R	A	M	m		All documentation stored in Preceptorship file
DD/MM/YY	Conference workshop	TRAMm Model for CPD with overview of HCPC standards	☐	☐	☐	1	2	3	4	☐	T	R	A	M	m		TRAMmCPD TRAMm Trail initiated (Date) Trail stored on CPD usb and updated (ongoing)
DD/MM/YY	Conference	Conference Day 2	C	☐	☐	1	2	☐	☐	☐	☐	☐	A	☐	☐	1	Attended Stroke Rehabilitation Seminar, TRAMmCPD workshop. CPD certificate of attendance stored in CPD file

Figure 7.1 Sally's TRAMm Tracker. Entries in green highlight updates from previous chapter.

TRAMm Trail

Please note: The TRAMm Trail has been designed for you to plan and record in a little more depth your most significant pieces of CPD. It is not anticipated that you would complete this for every piece of your CPD, only those you feel may be useful for evidence if called by the HCPC for audit. Remember to maintain confidentiality.

TRAMm Trail Title: Chapter 7: Career development planning   **Date: MM/YY – MM/YY**

Tell (T)	Record (R)	Activities (A)
• Informal discussions with mentor and manager regarding career progression (DD/MM/YY)	• SWOT Analysis stored on CPD usb (ongoing) • Goals explicitly recorded in supervision log (DD/MM/YY) • Reflection of current progression and future career plans using Boud model of reflection (DD/MM/YY – ongoing) • TRAMm Tracker updated (DD/MM/YY) • TRAMm Trail initiated (DD/MM/YY)	

Monitor (M)	Measure (m)	HCPC Standards met: 1, 2, 3, 4
• Mentorship meetings with Mentor to discuss and plan career development (DD/MM/YY) • Discussion and goal setting with line manager (DD/MM/YY) • Reflection of current progression and future career plans using Boud model of reflection (DD/MM/YY – ongoing)		PLAN of ACTION: • **Investigate placement educator course by DD/MM/YY** • **Investigate leadership opportunities** • **Update TRAMm Tracker (timescale)** • **Update TRAMm Trail (timescale)** • **Update Reflection after 3 Months**

Figure 7.2 Sally's TRAMm Trail: Career Development Planning

8

How do you measure your CPD?
TRAMm Station m: mEASURE

Remember, in TRAMm the 'm' denotes 'measure', purely to distinguish it from 'M' for 'monitor'. The lower-case 'm' does not have any significance in terms of relative importance.

Specific, individualised goals provide a baseline upon which the success of your CPD can be measured – for instance, through appraisal and performance review. This chapter discusses why measurement is a critical part of CPD, and how outcomes can be used to indicate progress and future direction. It identifies and explains mechanisms for measuring the outcomes of CPD, including the TRAMm Tracker and TRAMm Trail and goal/target setting, providing illustrations through case examples and completed Trackers. Instructions on how to make objectives SMART will also be given.

At the end of the chapter, tasks will provide opportunities for you to develop your own measurement baselines, explore ways to measure your CPD and to practise using the TRAMmCPD tools.

What do we mean by 'measure' (m)?

In Chapter 7 we explored the concept of monitoring, which was described as a formative process that relies upon constructive feedback or self-critique to facilitate professional development. While monitoring allows individuals to grow and develop, it is no longer acceptable simply to declare that professional development is taking place. Instead we need to provide evidence to demonstrate what development has occurred, how it has taken place, and the impact it has had. This evidence is achieved by measurement, which can take a variety of forms, the most common of which will be discussed in more detail below.

The International Accounting Education Standards Board (2008) describes two main types of measurement for CPD: input and output measurement. Input measurement measures the CPD undertaken – such as hours spent attending courses, credits received and certificates awarded.

However, professional bodies have now acknowledged that these input measurements do not actually demonstrate that anything has been learnt through the CPD; nor do they show that what has been learnt will be applied in practice and lead to change.

As part of the regulation process, the HCPC (2012a) CPD standards reflect the idea of output measurement. This refers to aspects such as measures of impact or, in other words, what has been achieved as a direct result of your CPD. If you revisit the HCPC CPD standards in Chapter 1, you will remember that standards 3 and 4 relate to application and impact, which could be interpreted in several ways in the environment in which you are working. These standards relate to:

- Your service users or other stakeholders (e.g. What has been the impact on a patient's independence or a student's exam results?)
- The organisation (e.g. Can you demonstrate an improvement in delivery of service? Is there a cost saving? Are patients being discharged earlier?)
- The staff of the organisation where you work (e.g. Did you implement something that improved working conditions or made something easier for staff?)
- Yourself? (e.g. Have you noticed an increase in your confidence? Have you developed a new skill that you are now applying in practice?)

Measurement is needed at both macro and micro levels, and we need to measure successes but also learn from any failures. For your CPD to be relevant or successful, it does not necessarily have to result in an improvement. Instead it may simply highlight that something is wrong or does not work, in which case stopping it or doing something differently might indirectly lead to a positive change. When submitting your evidence to the HCPC, they do not expect you to show that all your CPD has had significant benefit for service users. However, they will expect you to have considered why it has (or hasn't) benefited service users and, if appropriate, what you would do differently next time (HCPC 2012a).

Why do we need to measure CPD?

In Chapter 2 we discussed the importance of setting out our learning needs and being specific about our goals, but how do we know if we are achieving what we have set out to achieve? Whether it is to meet HCPC standards, organisational targets or objectives we have set for ourselves, there is no point in setting goals if we do not have in place some way to check that they have been met.

Since the introduction of Clinical Governance and the redefining of standards by the HCPC (2012a), CPD can be costly and resource intensive. As a result, outcome measurement for CPD is now required by a number of organisations (including professional and regulatory bodies), as well as managers across a range of sectors responsible for service delivery and the education of people in health and social care.

The HCPC (2012c), who are responsible for the audit of CPD for allied health professionals, states that CPD should not only be undertaken to influence practice but also to benefit service users. The meaning of the term 'service user' depends very much on the context in which the individual undertaking the CPD is working, as shown in Table 8.1 (below).

Table 8.1 Definition of service user versus context (HCPC 2012a)

Role	Example of work context	Service users
Practitioner/student practitioner	Hospital/social care setting/ward/ department/unit/patient's home/school/ care home	Patients or colleagues
Manager	Hospital/social care setting/ward/ department/unit/patient's home/school/ care home	Staff/colleagues/service users
Educator	University/placement setting	Students/colleagues
Researcher	University/laboratory/hospital/community	Participants/users of research

Once you have considered your work context, it is important to think about the sorts of things that require measurement. These may be as a result of requests from others (such as your manager or professional body) or to support developments for your service users (such as purchasing new equipment or providing new treatments). It may also be that you simply need evidence to support your CPD. Whatever the reason, the following sections will explore some of the aspects that can be measured and how.

What aspects of CPD can you measure?

There are many things you can measure in relation to CPD, depending on your particular role. These aspects are most effectively articulated by answering certain questions. The relevant questions will depend on the nature of the CPD you have undertaken and the context of your work. A few examples are given below.

Questions relating to the impact of your CPD on yourself:

● Has the CPD activity increased my knowledge and skills and influenced my practice?

● In what way has CPD influenced my practice?

● Has my level of confidence changed?

● What, if anything, would I do differently next time?

● Have I met the objectives I set for my CPD? If so, how?

- Can I place a tick against the first four HCPC standards?
- Have I visited every appropriate station for TRAMm?

Questions relating to the impact of your CPD on your service users:

- Has my CPD had an impact (positive or negative) on my service users?
- What specific impact has my CPD had on my service users?
- Are my patient outcomes significantly different since I undertook my CPD activity?
- How has my CPD impacted on the performance or ability of my service users?
- What do my service users think of my intervention?
- Have my peers or colleagues noticed any changes in service user performance?
- What, if anything, would I do differently next time?

Questions relating to the impact of your CPD on your organisation:

- Has my CPD had an impact on service delivery?
- How has my CPD had an impact on service delivery?
- Have I saved my organisation any money?
- Have I generated any income for my organisation?
- Have I influenced organisational strategy through my CPD?
- Has my CPD contributed to policy development?
- What, if anything, would I do differently next time?

Once you have decided on the question you wish to answer, there are various mechanisms that facilitate measurement. The following section gives a brief overview of each.

How do we measure CPD and what can we use as evidence?

In health and social care, the word 'evidence' features regularly and evidence-based practice is expected to underpin everything that we do. So what do we mean by evidence and how can we distinguish between 'good' and 'bad' evidence?

Researchers generally accept that there is a 'hierarchy of evidence' when you are considering the most appropriate material to use when evidencing CPD (Burns et al. 2011). However, while it is useful to consider these issues when evaluating and measuring your CPD, it is important not to get too concerned about the *type* of evidence; the *quality* of your evidence is always more important. While a systematic review, based on a meta-analysis of many studies, may be considered the best form of evidence from a research perspective, it is definitely not an appropriate way to evaluate an individual's CPD.

For allied health professionals, the HCPC is the regulatory body responsible for setting our standards for CPD (HCPC 2012c) and undertaking audit (see p. 121) to ensure that the standards are being met by registrants. You should consistently have these standards in the forefront of your mind during your CPD process (see Table 8.2).

If you are one of the 2.5% selected for audit in any given year (which for each professional group happens biennially), you will be required to renew your registration and submit a profile on an HCPC template. The first section asks you to outline your current role and responsibilities (approximately 500 words) and the second requires you to demonstrate your CPD and how it has met the standards, especially 3 and 4 (no more than 1500 words). This profile should be submitted with any evidence, together with a list of all CPD activities and dates undertaken in the last two years (HCPC 2012e). For full details of the HCPC audit process, see http://www.hpc-uk.org/registrants/cpd/audit/.

The HCPC has a range of resources in different formats to help you prepare your documentation if you are selected for audit as follows.

Table 8.2 Useful HCPC resources

Resource	How to access
HCPC (2012a) Continuing professional development and your registration	Free download available: http://www.hcpc-uk.org/assets/documents/10001314CPD_and_your_registration.pdf Copies also available in large print and Welsh. For hard copies, email: publications@hcpc-uk.org Tel: +44 (0)20 7840 9806
HCPC (2012c) Your guide to our standards for continuing professional development	Free download available: http://www.hcpc-uk.org/assets/documents/10001314CPD_and_your_registration.pdf Copies also available in large print and Welsh. For hard copies, email: publications@hcpc-uk.org Tel: +44 (0)20 7840 9806
HCPC (2012e) How to complete your continuing professional development profile	Free download available: http://www.hpc-uk.org/assets/documents/10002216How_to_fill_in_your_CPD_profile.pdf For hard copies, email: publications@hcpc-uk.org Tel: +44 (0)20 7840 9806
HCPC Video presentations on CPD	View at: http://www.hpc-uk.org/registrants/cpd/video/
HCPC sample profiles for each of the registered professions	Free download available: http://www.hpc-uk.org/registrants/cpd/sampleprofiles/

NB: All websites accessed 29 September 2015.

The most important thing to consider when deciding upon your evidence is the connection between what you are measuring or need to evidence and what you are using. For example, if you have been on a course and wish to demonstrate application of CPD in practice (HCPC, Standard 3), then a certificate will not suffice on its own. However, the certificate will form part of your evidence to show that a variety of CPD activities have been undertaken (HCPC, Standard 1).

When contemplating how to evidence what you have achieved through CPD, there are many different methods you can use. Table 8.3 provides an overview of the types of evidence you might wish to consider for each of the HCPC standards and the section that follows explains some of the core methods to help you to decide on an approach to measuring or evidencing your CPD.

Table 8.3 Types of evidence

HCPC standard	Type of evidence	Examples of evidence
1 Record of CPD	Dated list	● TRAMm Tracker ● Other CPD record form ● Professional Development Portfolio
2 Range of activities	Lists/authenticating documents	● Certificates ● Testimonials ● TRAMm Trail ● TRAMm Tracker ● Self-designed list ● Online record
3 Application in practice	Reflection	● Written reflection ● Extracts from supervision report
	Documentation	● Service evaluation reports ● Publications ● Research reports ● Quality Improvement Project reports ● Policy document or strategy highlighting contribution ● Case studies
	Service user feedback	● Group or intervention evaluations ● Research project/service evaluation ● Module/course feedback

3 Application in practice (cont.)	Feedback from manager/other	● Extract from appraisal ● Performance indicators ● Commendations/professional awards ● Accreditations, e.g. fellowships
4 Benefits for service user	Measured outcome	● Outcome measures ● Standardised assessments (before and after) ● Exam results and report
	Research	● Research reports/peer-reviewed articles
	Service user/carer/ feedback	● Anecdotal evidence ● Intervention evaluations ● Research project data reports ● Service evaluation reports
	Student evaluation	● National Student Survey ● Module/course/programme evaluations
5 Call for audit	Record of activity	● TRAMm Tracker ● Printed online record
	Variety of activities	● TRAMm Tracker ● TRAMm Trails ● Written profile ● CPD portfolio (if requested)
	Application in practice	● TRAMm Trail ● Reflective statement ● CPD portfolio (if requested)
	Benefit for service users	● Reflective statement, CPD portfolio (if requested)

Research

Research is one of the best forms of evidence in terms of application of CPD. In Chapter 6 we looked at research as a CPD activity and the benefits of this for your professional development. Research is probably considered to be the most rigorous means of measurement and there are many different types of research study, depending on the question that needs to be answered.

Contrary to popular belief, it is not necessary to undertake large randomised controlled trials if you wish to use research to evidence the impact of your CPD. If this were the case, very few of us would ever attempt to use research in this way. However, it *is* important that you select the correct methodology and ensure that your study is valid (tests what it is supposed to test) and reliable (the data collection 'tool' you use can produce the same results every time it is used). A small pilot project, which assures validity and reliability and acknowledges limitations, is much more valuable as evidence than a poorly conducted large study.

Firstly, you need to decide if you plan to undertake a research study or whether what you intend is not true research but instead an audit or service evaluation (Health Research Authority 2015). In short, a research study will usually involve the inclusion of something new or a manipulation of variables; an audit will benchmark something against predetermined standards; and a service evaluation is an evaluation of current practice as it stands. Audits and evaluations can still provide valuable evidence of CPD and procedures are often much simpler to follow than if full scientific approval is required. For more comprehensive details, see audits and service evaluations (pp. 125–6) or access the HRA website (http://www.hra.nhs.uk), which has a useful decision-making tool to help you clarify the nature of your study: http://www.hra-decisiontools.org.uk/research/

If you have never done research before or have only undertaken a small study as part of your university degree, don't let that put you off but get help from someone who understands the process and the pitfalls. In large organisations such as the NHS there are people whose role is to help you with research projects. On the other hand, if you are in a smaller unit or a non-traditional setting, you will need to think about others who may be able to provide research mentorship – for example, staff at your local university or a person who already has a research-based qualification such as a doctorate. You may find that this new partnership is mutually beneficial if the act of being a mentor can contribute towards the other person's CPD.

Collaborative projects are helpful, as a critical eye can often help you avoid some of the biases that may arise, particularly if you are researching something that you have designed or changed yourself. Many get drawn into the trap of trying to 'prove' that what they have done has had a positive impact and this can impede the trustworthiness of the study. Others forget to consider the presence of any confounding variables (such as other treatments, the environment or medication) that may be responsible for the success of the study, rather than the specific intervention that is being researched. Remember, even if a study discovers that what you have introduced has had no impact or a negative impact, it still gives evidence of the application of your CPD in practice and a development in knowledge and/or skills. Admittedly, this may initially be disappointing but may still benefit service users if you stop doing an unhelpful intervention or change how it is done. This is just as important as showing that something works.

Using research to evidence your CPD

As a health and care professional, it is expected that, even if you are not undertaking formal research, you should show how you have used research evidence to support your practice. Investigating and applying research evidence can be considered part of your CPD, but you must record how you have used it in order to demonstrate learning. See Example 8.1 (below).

Example 8.1 Using research as CPD

Imagine that you have attended a one-day course on mindfulness and you decide that this might be a useful intervention for some of your clients who are presenting with depression. You re-read the guidance that the trainers have given, regarding the implementation of mindfulness, and then undertake a search to explore whether any systematic reviews or other trustworthy research studies have highlighted specific conditions that are essential for its success. (For example, is it best done in a group or on a one-one basis? And how often should people practice?) You critique the studies to assure yourself that they are valid and reliable. You then map your findings onto an intervention evidence chart (see Table 8.4 below) to justify your practice and create an evidence file for mindfulness in your department.

Table 8.4: Example intervention evidence chart

Intervention	Application	Evidence (fictitious)
Mindfulness	● X sessions in total ● X mins per session ● Practice x times per week ● Depression/Anxiety ● X age group	Smith, A. & Jones, B. (2015). Undertaking mindfulness with people with depression and/or anxiety; a systematic review. *Journal of XXXXXX.* 1 (4), 238–56.
	● X technique ● Closed group ● Maximum 6 people ● Depression	Green, Z. (2014). Using XXXXXX technique to enable mindfulness for people with depression. *Journal of XXXXXX.* 13 (3), 134–45.

Audit

Audit is a crude, yet often useful, measurement of CPD for both the individual and the organisation. At one time, the term 'audit' was invariably associated with money. In healthcare, various audits are now undertaken such as clinical audit and documentary audit. Audits involve the systematic checking of standards against previously designed benchmarks in order to drive up quality in an organisation or individual.

In an organisation, audits offer an efficient way of providing valuable data regarding improvements in service delivery and associated tasks. For example, in relation to patient reports, standards are defined and a benchmark percentage stipulated (let's say, at least 93% of reports must meet the given standards at 100% accuracy). Following this, all reports are checked against the standards during a specified period. The outcome measure (usually delivered as a percentage of those that fully meet the standards) is then announced and compared against the benchmark percentage. Recommendations may then be made for improvement, and the benchmark percentage may be changed (usually in an upward direction) for the next audit.

In terms of your own CPD, the TRAMm Tracker could be used as your own mini audit. The boxes represent the standards, and the benchmark is set for the percentage of boxes ticked for each CPD activity; or 100% of boxes should be ticked across CPD activities during a specified period of time.

From a manager's or organisation's perspective, audit can also be applied to CPD. In Chapter 7, we discussed a range of suggestions for monitoring CPD, including the various activities undertaken or the number of hours taken by each staff member for CPD. Each of these could be subject to audit, either separately or combined as a CPD audit. Monitoring these aspects of CPD may include keeping a record through supervision, while an audit will provide an *actual* measure. This will be invaluable if you are required to provide reports for the organisation or professional bodies. As a manager, you may find the headings of the TRAMm Tracker useful to structure your audit tool. Alternatively, you may utilise TRAMmCPD to frame CPD within your department, and the audit could be based around staff completion of the Tracker and Trails, with percentage targets for completion of each of the boxes on the chart and numbers of Trails.

Service evaluation

A service evaluation is similar to research, in that you are investigating the impact of something, but the difference here is that you are not changing any of the variables or normal assessment or treatment approaches for the patients or stakeholders.

For example, let's say you run a six-week community memory group for patients who have early stage dementia. You always undertake a baseline assessment at the start of the group and re-do this at the end of the six weeks. Your evaluation will involve comparing scores before and after, and providing a report on the impact of this specific group. The findings will not be gene ralisable to any other similar group run elsewhere, either within your organisation or across other organisations.

We should be carrying this out as part of normal practice but evaluation formalises the process. The important thing is that you are not doing anything different from what you would normally do for current or new interventions. You use the same criteria for inclusion, you run the same types of sessions, and the assessments you undertake before and after are the same. Occasionally you may decide to measure an intervention (where you are not currently doing so) or introduce a new intervention, but this is what you are required to do as part of professional practice so it is still service evaluation.

Standardised assessments and outcome measures

Outcomes measures are essential in order to measure the impact of an intervention or programme on a service user, stakeholder or service. They are an important part of service delivery for all sectors or professionals who are keen to justify their role. It is important to use standardised assessments or outcome measures exactly as they are designed to be used; this will help to reduce some of the potential flaws in terms of validity. There is a danger that, if you design your own assessment tool without piloting, you may get results that do not accurately depict the real outcome. For example, when your service user is discharged, how do you know that this has been due to your professional intervention rather than that of the team or another profession?

Grant (1999) highlighted the fact that outcome measures are also important for measuring the impact of professional development, although the process can be complex. Finding measures that evidence the impact of CPD on attitudes and practice requires a different approach from those needed to evidence impact on service users. Measurements of effect on service users are usually based on evaluation tools and professional judgements.

Appraisals/individual performance reviews/professional development reviews

Appraisals are a requirement of most large health and care organisations for all staff and are usually undertaken by a person's line manager once every six to twelve months. In some organisations, appraisals are linked to performance-related pay, but for health and care workers the aim of appraisals is generally to ensure that all staff are developing appropriately according to their level of responsibility and working in line with the strategic direction of the organisation. Having an appraisal system in place also demonstrates the organisation's commitment to CPD.

If carried out correctly, the appraisal process will involve opportunities for review partway through the appraisal period. In addition, appraisal should not be used as an opportunity for initial discussions regarding any concerns about performance; these should be highlighted as and when they arise, rather than waiting for a scheduled appraisal. Progress with professional development in relation to concerns previously highlighted may, however, form part of the discussion.

The appraisal process usually focuses on four main areas:

1. Clarifying the main current and aspirational roles of the appraisee

2. Reviewing the objectives set in the previous appraisal, alongside the evidence to support achievement

3. Identifying any performance limiting or supporting factors in relation to the workplace

4. Setting new objectives for the forthcoming period, together with personal training and development needs.

In order to ensure that the appraisal process works for you and supports or evidences your professional development, it is important to give careful thought to preparing for your appraisal meeting. With this aim in mind, it is useful to take stock of your current roles and responsibilities, reflect upon how they link with your own preferred or aspirational profile, consider your achievements since the last appraisal and summarise your evidence for this. It is also important to carefully consider your future objectives and training or development needs. When you put these together you must ensure that:

● The objectives are written using a SMART format to enable non-contested discussions as to whether or not they have been achieved (see Chapter 2)

● The objectives give due consideration to the strategic direction of your department and wider organisation

● At least one or two objectives are related to the application of CPD and having a direct or indirect impact on service users or stakeholders

● The objectives reflect (in part or in full) your aspirations for professional development. Even if you do not intend to do everything in the forthcoming period, it is useful to begin to 'hint' about your aspirations. For example, you may not wish to start your PhD this year but an objective might be to investigate possible areas for research.

Measuring informal learning

Informal learning occurs when you least expect it. It may be something that is explained or debated in the staffroom, a discussion over lunch with a colleague, an observation made in the community or an incident or issue via a television programme. This learning is no less valuable even though it can be difficult to measure or assess (Mathers *et al.* 2012). If you are wishing to evidence this, the most effective option is to undertake a written reflection that identifies the source of the learning, what it has helped you to understand and how this learning has influenced or will influence your practice and/or benefit your service users or stakeholders.

Preceptorship

In Chapter 7 we introduced the concept of preceptorship and how it can be used to monitor progress. Preceptorship can also be a mechanism for measurement, as successful progress through individual professional development plans linked to the Knowledge and Skills Framework (KSF) leads to incremental advance. Successful achievement of preceptorship offers measurable evidence that you have reached the standard required for working in that organisation.

Records are kept throughout preceptorship to provide evidence that the process has occurred and that CPD has taken place. These records can then be used to provide the evidence required to sign-off on final completion.

A similar process in other organisations is called 'probation'. Again this occurs for a defined period of time (usually 12–36 months), during which time the individual has regular meetings with a line manager who is responsible for overseeing the individual's professional development. Successful completion of probation can lead to a full contract of employment and/or a higher pay band.

Peer review and measurement

As we saw in Chapter 7, peer review can take many forms and can either make up part of the monitoring process or provide a way of measuring CPD. Although some aspects of peer review provide a measurement of organisational progress, they can also be used as evidence of your own performance. Examples of this are given below.

One type of summative peer review is the self-regulation by qualified members of a profession from the same field. An example of this might be accreditation, where in healthcare education, and normally every five years, any degree programme leading to a professional award is subject to review by fellow colleagues to ensure its fitness for the award it is conferring. During this process, formative feedback may be offered but there is also an outcome in terms of whether the programme is approved. This may involve commendations, conditions (which must be addressed) and/or recommendations (which must be given consideration). At the end of the process, a final decision is taken as to whether the professional body is happy to accredit the programme for a further specified period of time.

Another type of summative peer review assesses suitability for publication (e.g. in a journal or book) or presentation (e.g. at a conference). In this instance, the outcome or measurement is the decision as to whether or not the work is accepted.

Taking part in peer review can be considered a CPD activity, whether you are the reviewee or reviewer, and the outcome of the review can provide valuable evidence regarding your professional development. For example, let's say you have led a programme review and preparation of documentation for accreditation, and the organisation receives feedback that the new programme presented demonstrates innovation and full team engagement in the planning. You could then use this as evidence of your developing leadership ability and it may also be used as evidence of achievement of one of your outcomes set at appraisal. Likewise, if a paper you have written is accepted for publication, you could use this as evidence of your ability to undertake research or measurement in terms of dissemination of CPD.

Measurements required by organisations

In 2006, the World Health Organisation described six dimensions defining quality, where improvement should continually be sought. One of these was the need for care to be efficient (maximising resources and avoiding waste). At a macro level, organisations are not only interested in the success of your CPD benefiting the service as a whole but also the cost-effectiveness of such intervention. There is limited evidence to support the cost-effectiveness of CPD. However, the alternative to CPD, the implementation of unsupported interventions, could be considered a wasteful use of resources in itself.

Quality-adjusted life years (QALYs) are defined and described by the National Institute for Health and Care Excellence (NICE) (2015) as:

> A measure of the state of health of a person or group in which the benefits, in terms of length of life, are adjusted to reflect the quality of life. One QALY is equal to 1 year of life in perfect health. QALYs are calculated by estimating the years of life remaining for a patient following a particular treatment or intervention and weighting each year with a quality of life score (on a zero to 1 scale). It is often measured in terms of the person's ability to perform the activities of daily life, freedom from pain and mental disturbance.

QALYs may therefore offer a useful unit of measurement if you are attempting to demonstrate the cost-effectiveness of a specific intervention designed during CPD, but experience is required with their use, so it is recommended that advice is sought before you consider utilising them.

In most cases it is probably more appropriate to measure how much money your CPD has cost. You can then balance this information against, for example, discharge times versus cost of hospital beds per day, money saved on staff time if procedures have been streamlined, or income generated versus the cost of undertaking CPD. Your manager, finance or research department should be able to help you consider ways in which these comparisons can be most effectively calculated.

For those of us providing health care, it is impossible to avoid risk altogether and patients may occasionally undergo treatments where there is the potential for harm. However, patients and service users do have a right to expect care from skilled and knowledgeable staff who help them to decide what is best in their case (Royal College of Nursing et al. 2007). Patient safety should be a core focus of any organisation. As a result, any CPD where application of learning might help to increase patient safety is considered important. This impact must be measurable in some way, though it is not always easy to link it to CPD.

Safety can be measured both quantitatively and from a qualitative perspective. Using quantitative methodologies often involves setting of targets and measuring their compliance – for example, incident reporting, cases of infection following an audit approach (see p. 125). The National Advisory group on the Safety of Patients in England (2013) highlights the limitations of this approach in certain instances (such as reporting incidents) where non-reporting or inaccurate reporting leads to inaccurate data. Instead, Brown and Lilford (2008) advocate the use of a mixed methods approach in order to both define the problems and measure impact.

Measurement may take the form of research or evaluations, and these quality improvement projects are often useful to address issues of patient safety. Subsequent reports can provide excellent evidence of CPD in relation to HCPC Standards 3 and 4.

Using informal or anecdotal evidence

Formal types of evidence (as detailed on pp. 123–30) are much easier to produce, but it is often informal anecdotal evidence from service users that provides us with the most immediate feedback.

However, it is difficult to know how to use anecdotal evidence, particularly if you are selected for audit. So how do we use and record anecdotal material as evidence?

Some types of anecdotal evidence may be abstract aspects, such as time or confidence. Your reflections may reveal that you feel more confident undertaking a skill or activity, or you realise that you have become much quicker at completing what was once a more time-consuming task.

Before you start using anecdotal evidence, remember: you are bound by your professional body and the HCPC to respect confidentiality when reporting anything. If you are ever unsure about the necessity of this, err on the side of caution and do not use names or any other significant identifying features.

There are several ways to do this, as listed in Table 8.5 below.

Table 8.5: Referencing anecdotal evidence

Type of evidence	How to capture NB: All need to be anonymised versions for submission (HCPC 2012d).
Conversation with service users, carers or students; feedback	Document this in case notes, or have it recorded in supervision or appraisal records
Confidence or time taken to perform a task or skill	Reflect on how your confidence has increased and the time taken to perform the task or skill has decreased
Emails	Anonymise first, then print off the email/s
References or testimonials	Request permission from the provider and submit permission with the document
Feedback via social media	Take screenshots and use online information collation and digital curation tools (see Chapters 4, 5 or 6), anonymised as appropriate
Text feedback	Screenshot and either digitally anonymise or remove identification and photocopy
Cards/Letters of thanks	Anonymise first, then photocopy or print out

All the above could also be captured in your reflections, documented as quotes to support what you are saying.

Using TRAMmCPD to measure CPD

Some examples of how the TRAMm Tracker and Trail can be used to measure or evidence CPD have been identified above and details of their completion are given in Chapter 5.

The TRAMm Tracker has been designed to be used as an 'at-a-glance' record of engagement in CPD, which can be submitted as your CPD record during the HCPC audit process. It is easy to identify CPD undertaken, and where there is potential for further development. The Tracker enables you to record formal and informal activities carried out, and identify any gaps in terms of maintaining or reaching HCPC standards or missing visits to TRAMm stations.

Although the TRAMm Trail does not provide any specific measurement, it offers a more detailed summary of the more significant activities and station visits. They can be completed fairly quickly, as a reminder of the evidence you have, or the evidence you still need to collect.

From the feedback we have had from the pilot evaluation, people have found it most effective to use their TRAMm Tracker and TRAMm Trail as 'works in progress', updating them as they go along. They have used them in their supervision sessions and annual appraisals to highlight what has been achieved and identify their learning needs.

TRAMmCPD can help you identify your learning needs by highlighting the gaps and encouraging you to consider how they can be addressed. The decision as to which TRAMm station each element of CPD fits into is entirely subjective, although suggestions are included as to what might be appropriate in each chapter. This also applies to meeting the HCPC CPD standards (see Example 8.2). To further help your decision, it is important that you consider the following questions:

1. How does this station or standard relate to the specific aspect of CPD?
2. Can you justify why it fits into the station or under the standard?
3. What evidence can you produce to support this?

Example 8.2 Does supervision meet all the HCPC standards?

Question from practitioner: In the TRAMmCPD information available on your website, it states that supervision only covers HCPC Standards 1 and 2. However, I would argue that supervision covers all 4 standards. Here are my reasons.

Practitioner justification – HCPC Standard 1
Yes: completing my TRAMm Tracker demonstrates that I am maintaining a continuing, up-to-date and accurate record of my CPD activities.

TRAMm mentor response: Yes I agree.
Practitioner justification – HCPC Standard 2
Yes: My TRAMm Tracker demonstrates I am carrying out a mixture of learning activities.

TRAMm mentor response: Yes I agree.
Practitioner justification – HCPC Standard 3
Yes: By participating in supervision, I am ensuring that my CPD has contributed to the quality of my practice.

TRAMm mentor response: Not necessarily. Where is your evidence to show that your supervision session has considered the application of your CPD specifically, rather than normal work practice? If you can justify how, then you can tick this box.

(See Chapters 3 and 5 for discussion regarding when normal work becomes CPD.)

Practitioner justification – HCPC Standard 4

Yes: Regular supervision obviously benefits my service users through discussion of their needs and my interventions.

TRAMm mentor response: Not necessarily. Talking about it and doing it are two very different things. Firstly, are your discussions reflective, critical and suggesting action points? Or are you just having a chat about your normal work practice? Where is your evidence to show that you have learnt something from the supervision that is contributing to your CPD, that you have applied it in practice and there has been an impact on your service user/s?

(See Chapters 3 and 5.)

Bear in mind that not all your learning experiences will address all the TRAMm stations. This should not be a matter for concern – as long as you are visiting all stations deemed appropriate over time, can justify why others are not appropriate, and can ensure that you visit all stations across the range of CPD you undertake.

Case study: Sally collates evidence for her portfolio

Sally is an occupational therapist. Over the last 24 months, she has progressed from being complacent about CPD to becoming fully engaged in the process, using TRAMmCPD as her guide. She has now developed a sound CPD profile, which is easy to access, and she has evidence in case she is called for HCPC audit or is required to complete any applications for future posts in her field. She has completed rotation posts in the areas of orthopaedics, mental health and neuro-rehabilitation, and she is just about to finish her fourth rotation in rheumatology. She is hoping that a Band 6 position in the field of neuro-rehabilitation will soon become available. In the meantime, she is continuing with activities to develop her skills and profile accordingly.

Sally meets the occupational therapy manager for her first proper appraisal since she started this post and completed her preceptorship 12 months ago. They review the objectives she set 12 months ago and Sally begins to realise how much she has changed in her approach to CPD, her professionalism and her knowledge and skills since her final preceptorship review.

Using her TRAMm Tracker and TRAMm Trails to frame her discussion, she highlights the CPD she has measurements for, and presents her evidence to her line manager as follows:

1. She has her certificate of attendance for the conference where she attended her first TRAMmCPD workshop and a stroke rehabilitation seminar.

Evidence: In relation to application and benefit to users of TRAMmCPD, Sally produces her TRAMm Trail and talks through the CPD activities she has undertaken that have had a positive impact on her practice. She also shows the manager some feedback she has had following the presentation she did for her peers. She notes that four of them are now using TRAMmCPD and have set up a TRAMm support group, with Sally as the main facilitator.

2. She has a certificate for the two-day training course she undertook on neuro-developmental approaches.

Evidence: Anecdotal, comprising positive verbal feedback received from her neuro-rehabilitation mentor, which has been explicitly documented in Sally's supervision record, which she shows to her line manager.

3. Sally has designed and implemented a written 'return to driving after stroke pathway'.

Evidence: A clear concise written pathway for returning to driving following neurological deficit; a case study that illustrates a patient's experience when following the pathway. A quality improvement award received for excellent practice.

Her manager highlights the enormous progress Sally has made which, this year, has included achievements over and above the objectives that were set the previous year.

They discuss and agree new objectives for the forthcoming year, and Sally's manager says she will happily support any applications Sally makes for Band 6 positions in the future.

Tasks

- Consider the measurement tools you currently know about or use in your work, and think about how they could be used to measure aspects of your own CPD.

- Make a note for your next appraisal or performance review to ensure that your objectives are SMART and contain at least one objective that relates to the application of your planned CPD.

- Consider a specific question that you wish to answer, and identify an appropriate methodology by which to measure it. Decide if this is research, audit or service evaluation.

- Consider ways in which you could use your CPD to make cost savings for your organisation, or how you might use it to generate some income. Think about how you might show the cost effectiveness of your CPD in either situation.

- Complete the measurement section for at least one TRAMm Trail, and consider the measurements you may already have for the specific activity and your plans to measure in the future.

- Update your TRAMm Tracker.

- Read Chapter 9 to understand the key messages from each chapter in this book.

TRAMm TRACKER Chapter 8: *Updated tracker* Name: Sally OT

Date	Subject	Description	Certificate	Reflection	TRAMm Trail	HCPC 1	2	3	4	5	T	R	A	M	m	Index	Notes
DD/MM/YY	Service Development	Design and implementation of return to driving pathway following stroke	C	R	T	1	2	3	4	☐	T	R	A	M	m	3, 4	TRAMm Trail: Stored on CPD usb. Quality improvement award (3) and training Certificate (4) in CPD portfolio
DD/MM/YY	Planning	Career development planning with mentor and supervisor	☐	☐	T	1	2	☐	☐	☐	T	R	☐	M	☐		TRAMm Trail: Stored on CPD usb. Certificate in CPD portfolio
DD/MM/YY	Two day training course	Neuro-developmental approaches	C	☐	T	1	2	3	4	☐	T	R	☐	M	m	2	TRAMm Trail: Stored on CPD usb. Certificate in CPD portfolio
DD/MM/YY	Self-directed Learning	Rotation into Neurological Rehabilitation	☐	R	T	1	2	3	4	☐	T	R	A	M	m		See TRAMm Trail: Rotation into Neurological Rehabilitation. Stored on CPD usb
DD/MM/YY	Preceptorship	Preceptorship completed	☐	☐	☐	1	2	3	4	☐	T	R	A	M	m		All documentation stored in Preceptorship file
DD/MM/YY	Conference workshop	TRAMm Model for CPD with overview of HCPC standards	☐	☐	☐	1	2	3	4	☐	T	R	A	M	m		TRAMmCPD TRAMm Trail initiated (Date) Trail stored on CPD usb and updated (ongoing)

Figure 8.1 Sally's TRAMm Tracker. Entries in green highlight updates from previous chapter.

135

TRAMm Trail

Please note: The TRAMm Trail has been designed for you to plan and record in a little more depth your most significant pieces of CPD. It is not anticipated that you would

complete this for every piece of your CPD, only those you feel may be useful for evidence if called by the HCPC for audit. Remember to maintain confidentiality.

TRAMm Trail Title: Chapter 8: Service Development - Return to driving pathway following stroke   **Date: MM/YY – MM/YY**

Tell (T)	Record (R)	Activities (A)
• Informal discussions with manager of the ABI Team for advice when consultants have requested inappropriate assessment of patients (DD/MM/YY - ongoing)	• CPD certificate of attendance from training event (DD/MM/YY) (Index 3 in CPD file)	• Request from Consultant resulted in joint Rookwood Battery being completed with a patient (DD/MM/YY)
• Provided verbal feed back to the Team leader, in-patient therapy lead and therapy services manager about existence of the Rookwood Driving Battery and potential benefit to our service (DD/MM/YY – ongoing)	• Reflection using Rogers Reflective Cycle completed from fitness to drive training (CPD usb) (DD/MM/YY)	• Attended the training on the latest issues and guidance around driving fitness hosted by Acquired Brain Injury Service and Driving Assessment Centre (DD/MM/YY)
• Fed back information acquired from ABI training to Senior OT informally (DD/MM/YY).	• Rookwood record forms completed and filed in patient notes (DD/MM/YY).	• Rookwood used as cognitive assessment for patients wishing to return to driving (DD/MM/YY) to support their consultant's decision making process.
• Discussed increased use of Rookwood in our service during supervision (DD/MM/YY)	• Feed back to GP's and consultants with results and concerns in patients discharge letters (DD/MM/YY).	• Joint visit to patient with senior OT to demonstrate use of Rookwood (DD/MM/YY) Arranged meeting with ABI Neuro Psychologist, Therapies Manager
• Informally discussed plans for returning to driving pathway Stroke Association (DD/MM/YY).	• Case notes documented in patients notes (DD/MM/YY).	and Senior OT to discuss governance around our role in returning to driving and legal requirements etc. (DD/MM/YY)
• Verbal feedback to patients re concerns about the impact of cognitive deficits on their ability to return to driving (DD/MM/YYs)	• TRAMm Trail initiated (DD/MM/YY) and updated (ongoing) to be used in annual appraisal.	• Meeting with Senior OT to start writing returning to driving pathway (DD/MM/YY)
• Posts questions on social media to see what others have set up or are already doing (DD/MM/YY)	• Collated record of social media interactions (DD/MM/YY)	
• Meet with Snr OT to start pathway and feedback progress to Therapies Manager	• Supervision Records (DD/MM/YY)	
	• Clear concise written pathway for returning to driving following neurological deficit	
	• TRAMm Tracker (DD/MM/YY)	

TRAMm Trail

Please note: The TRAMm Trail has been designed for you to plan and record in a little more depth your most significant pieces of CPD. It is not anticipated that you would complete this for every piece of your CPD, only those you feel may be useful for evidence if called by the HCPC for audit. Remember to maintain confidentiality.

Monitor (M)	Measure (m)	HCPC Standards met: 1, 2, 3, 4
• Informal supervision with team manager to support progress and monitor pathway progression (DD/MM/YY) • Formal supervision with Senior OT (DD/MM/YY) • Self-monitoring using Rogers Reflective Cycle reflection • Pathway trialled and outcomes discussed with team manager	• Improved service to patients with clear concise written pathway for returning to driving following neurological deficit (DD/MM/YY) • Case study completed to illustrate patient journey/experience when following driving pathway (DD/MM/YY) • Quality improvement award received from excellent practice Certificate stored in CPD Portfolio Index 4 (DD/MM/YY)	**PLAN of ACTION:** • Feedback to Stroke Unit therapists, Stroke consultants and Stroke Association. • Update Reflection

Figure 8.2 Sally's TRAMm Trail: Service development (with thanks to Natalie Latham)

9

Conclusion

Continuing professional development is a personal journey. This handbook has been written for health and care professionals to illustrate the use of the **TRAMm** model and its tools, the **TRAMm Tracker** and **TRAMm Trail**, while also providing a comprehensive guide to encourage your strategic engagement in **CPD**. The key messages from each chapter are summarised below.

1. What is CPD and why do we do it?

In this chapter we explored the nature of CPD, and why we must engage in it as health or social care professionals.

Key messages

- As a health and social care professional, CPD is mandatory and is regulated by the HCPC for allied health professionals.

- CPD is your responsibility as a professional but can be facilitated by a number of people as well as your organisation.

- In order to demonstrate CPD, you must show its application in practice and its impact on your service users, according to the HCPC Standards for CPD (HCPC 2012c).

- There are a number of organisations you can contact, both national and international.

2. Engaging in CPD and developing your learning style

Here we explored why understanding your learning styles, and addressing CPD in a way that reflects your learning preferences, will help you to engage with it more effectively.

Key messages

- CPD is a personal journey and there is no such thing as 'one size fits all'.

- There are various tests and activities available that can help you identify your preferred learning style and ways to maximise learning opportunities.

- For CPD to be most effective, you must identify your learning needs and articulate these objectively to ensure they are measurable.
- Applying your learning in practice is an essential requisite of being a health and care professional.

3. Introduction to the TRAMm model

This chapter introduced mechanisms for strategic CPD, using TRAMmCPD.

Key messages

- Doing CPD is not the same as engaging in CPD.
- CPD is important for job satisfaction, quality of practice and its impact on service users.
- TRAMmCPD consists of a model to guide your approach, and tools (TRAMm Tracker and Trail) to record and measure your progress.
- TRAMmCPD can help you plan and execute appropriate professional development to meet your needs, along with those of your service users and the organisation in which you work.

4. How do you plan and disseminate your CPD? TRAMm Station T: TELL

Communication is a vital part of CPD, which helps you to plan and disseminate your learning so that it can be effective and benefit others.

Key messages

- Planning is essential. It can be formal or informal and goals may be strategic or designed for the short term.
- Plans should not be concrete but, instead, fluid and adaptable to change.
- Disseminating your learning is your professional responsibility.
- There are many ways to disseminate information, depending on your preference and the information you wish to impart.

5. How do you record your CPD plans and activities? TRAMm Station R: RECORD

This chapter explored why it is important to document your CPD and the different mechanisms you can use to record your CPD .

Key messages

- Various recording mechanisms are available to suit your individual preference, including written, visual, verbal and virtual media.

- The TRAMm Tracker provides a continuous record of CPD undertaken and may be used as part of your submission for HCPC audit.
- The TRAMm Trail provides greater depth of information regarding specific areas of learning, which can be used for planning and recording your CPD.
- The TRAMm Trail can provide an immediate prompt for your reflections .

6. What counts as CPD? TRAMm Station A: ACTIVITY

There is a huge range of activities that can be used to further your professional development.

Key messages

- Engaging in any form of activity can be effective if it is suited to your particular learning needs.
- Individuals often engage in activities that contribute towards their professional development and do so without realising that they are undertaking CPD.
- When planning your CPD, ensure the activities you select benefit you, your organisation and your service users and are recorded in your TRAMm Tracker and Trail.
- CPD activities do not have to cost money; there are many that are freely available.

7. How do you keep track of your CPD? TRAMm Station M: MONITOR

It is essential to monitor your progress in order to ensure that your professional development is a continuous journey.

Key messages

- Self-monitoring is vital. It involves taking stock of what you have achieved, and considering your short- and long-term aspirations.
- Ways of monitoring CPD include supervision, mentorship, preceptorship, peer review and reflection.
- It is important to document the monitoring progress and outcomes.
- The TRAMm Tracker and Trail can be used to monitor your progress and facilitate progress discussions.

8. How do you measure your CPD? TRAMm Station m: mEASURE

The outcomes of your CPD can be measured in a variety of ways and this provides evidence to indicate your progress and future direction.

Key messages

● TRAMmCPD encourages an output measurement approach, focused on the way you implement your learning.

● Setting SMART goals gives you a baseline from which to measure the success of your CPD.

● The TRAMm Tracker measures your performance in relation to HCPC standards and TRAMm stations.

● TRAMmCPD can help you structure your evidence if you are selected for HCPC audit.

All the key messages have been incorporated in each chapter in our continuous case study, where we have used TRAMmCPD to illustrate Sally's progressive engagement in the concept of CPD.

Continuing the CPD journey

You should now have a clear understanding of your learning style, the HCPC requirements for CPD and how to use TRAMmCPD to help you develop a strategy to advance your personal and professional journey over the next 12 months – and the next 5–10 years.

Our own journey continues, as we develop TRAMmCPD, and we welcome your queries and feedback. A research project has been initiated, evaluating the success of TRAMmCPD in supporting engagement in CPD.

Good luck on your CPD journey and remember that the TRAMmCPD tools are free to download from www.TRAMmCPD.com

References

Academy of Medical Royal Colleges (AMRC) (2010). *The Effectiveness of Continuing Professional Development (Final Report)*. London: General Medical Council.

Allied Health Professions Project (2003). *Demonstrating Competence through CPD*.
http://webarchive.nationalarchives.gov.uk/20130107105354/http://www.dh.gov.uk/prod_consum_dh/groups/dh_digitalassets/@dh/@en/documents/digitalasset/dh_4071462.pdf (Accessed 28 May 2014).

Alsop, A. (2013). *Continuing Professional Development in Health and Social Care. Strategies for Lifelong Learning*. 2nd edn. Chichester: Wiley-Blackwell.

Bargagliotti, A.L. (2012). Work engagement in nursing: a concept analysis. *Journal of Advanced Nursing*. **68** (6), 1414–28.

Blogg, D. & Challis, M. (2013). *Evidencing CPD: A Guide to Building your Social Work Portfolio (Critical Skills in Social Work)*. London: Critical Publishing Ltd.

Bodell, S. & Hook, A. (2011). Using Facebook for professional networking: a modern-day essential. *British Journal of Occupational Therapy*. **74** (12) 588–590

Boud, D. (1988). *Developing Student Autonomy in Learning*. London: Routledge, Kegan Paul.

Brown, C. & Lilford, R. (2008). Evaluating service delivery interventions to enhance patient safety. *British Medical Journal*. **337**:a2764.

Canadian Institutes of Health Research (CIHR) (2005). *Developing a CIHR framework to measure the impact of health research* (CIHR synthesis report).
http://www.ktdrr.org/ktlibrary/articles_pubs/ncddrwork/focus/focus18/Focus18.pdf (Accessed 7 September 2014).

Care Quality Commission (CQC) (2013). *Supporting information and guidance: Supporting effective clinical supervision*. http://www.cqc.org.uk/sites/default/files/documents/20130625_800734_v1_00_supporting_information-effective_clinical_supervision_for_publication.pdf (Accessed 7 April 2015).

Chartered Society of Physiotherapy (CSP) (2013). *Clinical supervision: a brief overview*.
https://v3.pebblepad.co.uk/v3portfolio/csp/Asset/View/6jqbh3GzhGWrfMMd9zc4ts3Mkc (Accessed 7 April 2015).

College of Occupational Therapists (COT) (2010). *Management briefing, supervision*. London: COT.

College of Occupational Therapists (COT) (2015). *Introduction to Social Media*. London: COT.

Constable, G. (2013). 'Reflection as a Catalyst in the Development of Personal and Professional Effectiveness' in D. Blogg & M. Challis (eds) *Evidencing CPD: A Guide to Building Your Social Work Portfolio*. Northwich: Critical Publishing. 53–69.

Critical Appraisal Skills Programme (CASP) (2015). *Making Sense of Evidence*.
http://www.casp-uk.net/ (Accessed 26 April 2015).

Cusick, A. & McCluskey, A. (2000). Becoming an evidence-based practitioner through professional development. *Australian Occupational Therapy Journal*. **47**, 159–70.

Davies, C.H.F. III., Regina Deli-Amen, R., Rios-Aguilar, C. & Gonzalez Canche, M.S. (2012). *Social Media in Higher Education: A Literature and Research Directions*. Arizona: University of Arizona and Claremont Graduate University.

Davis, D., Evans, M., Jadad, A., Perrier, L., Rath, D., Ryan, D., Sibbald, G., Straus, S., Rappolt, S., Wowk, M. & Zwarenstein, M. (2003). The case for knowledge translation: shortening the journey from evidence to effect. *British Medical Journal*. **327**, 33–35.

Delors, J. (1996). *Learning: The Treasure Within*. Paris. UNESCO.
http://www.norrag.org/es/publications/boletin-norrag/online-version/a-world-of-reports-a-critical-review-of-global-development-reports-with-an-angle-on-education-and-training/detail/the-delors-commission-and-report.html
(Accessed 25 April 2015).

Department of Health (DH) (1998). *The New NHS: Modern, Dependable*. London: The Stationery Office.

Department of Health (DH) (2001). *Our Healthier Nation: A Contract for Health*. London: The Stationery Office.

Department of Health (DH) (2002). *Learning from Bristol: The Department of Health's Response to the Report of the Public Inquiry into Children's Heart Surgery at the Bristol Royal Infirmary 1984–1995*.
https://www.gov.uk/government/uploads/system/uploads/attachment_data/file/273320/5363.pdf
(Accessed 30 September 2015).

Department of Health (DH) (2004). *Agenda for Change Final Agreement*
http://webarchive.nationalarchives.gov.uk/20130107105354/http://www.dh.gov.uk/en/Publicationsandstatistics/Publications/PublicationsPolicyAndGuidance/DH_4095943 (Accessed 9 October 2015).

Department of Health (DH) (2010). *Preceptorship Framework for Newly Registered Midwives, Nurses and AHPs.*
https://www.rcn.org.uk/__data/assets/pdf_file/0010/307756/Preceptorship_framework.pdf
(Accessed 30 September 2015).

Dixon-Woods, M. (2010). Why is patient safety so hard? A selective review of ethnographic studies. *Journal of Health Services and Research Policy.* **15** (1), 11–16.

Fish, D. & Twinn, S. (1997). *Quality Supervision in the Health Care Professions. Principled Approaches to Practice.* Oxford: Butterworth-Heinemann.

Fleming, N.D. & Mills, C. (1992). Not another inventory, rather a catalyst for reflection. *To Improve the Academy.* **11**, 137–55.

Gibbs, G. (1988). *Learning by Doing: a Guide to Teaching and Learning Methods.* Oxford Further Education Unit

Global eSchools and Communities Initiative (GeSCI) (2009). *Strategic Plan 2009–2011: Building a Knowledge Society for All.* http://www.gesci.org/assets/files/Strategic%20Plan%2009%20-11.pdf (Accessed 2 May 2015).

Gopee, N. (2015). *Mentoring and Supervision in Healthcare.* 3rd edn. London: Sage Publications Ltd.

Gould, D., Drey, N. & Berridge, E.J. (2007). Nurses' experiences of continuing professional development. *International Journal of Nursing Studies.* **27** (6), 602–609.

Grant, J. (1999). Measurement of learning outcomes in continuing professional development. *The Journal of Continuing Education in the Health Professions.* **19**, 214–21.

Health and Care Professions Council (HCPC) (2012a). *Continuing Professional Development and Your Registration.* London: HCPC.

Health and Care Professions Council (HCPC) (2012b). *Standards of Conduct, Performance and Ethics.* London: HCPC.

Health and Care Professions Council (HCPC) (2012c). *Your Guide to Our Standards for Continuing Professional Development.* London: HCPC.

Health and Care Professions Council (HCPC) (2012d). *Confidentiality – Guidance for Registrants.* London: HCPC.

Health and Care Professions Council (HCPC) (2012e). *How to Complete your Continuing Professional Development Profile.* London: HCPC.

Health and Care Professions Council (HCPC) (2014a). *About Registration.* http://www.hcpc-uk.org/aboutregistration/professions/index.asp?id=16#profDetails (Accessed 23 April 2014).

Health and Care Professions Council (HCPC) (2014b). *Continuing Professional Development Audit Report 2011–2013.* London: HCPC

Health and Care Professions Council (HCPC) (2015a). *Preventing Small Problems from Becoming Big Problems in Health and Social Care.* London: HCPC.

Health and Care Professions Council (HCPC) (2015b). *Focus on Standards – Social Networking Sites.* London: HCPC. http://www.hcpc-uk.org/Assets/documents/100035B7Social_media_guidance.pdf (Accessed 26 April 2015).

Health and Care Professions Council (HCPC) (2015c). *Frequently Asked Questions.* http://www.hpc-uk.org/registrants/cpd/faqs/ (Accessed 19 April 2015).

Health and Safety Executive (2015). *Stress-related and Psychological Disorders in Great Britain 2014.* http://www.hse.gov.uk/statistics/causdis/stress/index.htm (Accessed 30 April 2015).

Health Research Authority (HRA) (2015). Home Page. http://www.hra.nhs.uk (Accessed 25 April 2015).

Hearle, D. (2015). *CPD Engagement: A Concept Analysis* (unpublished)

Honey, P. & Mumford, A. (1992). *The Manual of Learning Styles.* Maidenhead: Peter Honey.

Holdsworth, L., Douglas, D., Hunter, E. & McDonald, C. (2013). Social Media: Raising the Profile of AHPs. *British Journal of Healthcare Management.* **19** (2), 85–92.
http://www.magonlinelibrary.com/doi/abs/10.12968/bjhc.2013.19.2.85 (Accessed 20 April 2015).

International Accounting Education Standards Board (IAESB) (2008). *Approaches to Continuing Professional Development (CPD) – An Information Paper.*
https://docs.google.com/document/d/1oi1pMOFJUGC8HS3aBqigDaUlKJqACvQdvpyzWCr1PjY/edit (Accessed 10 April 2015).

Jamieson, L., Harris, L. & Hall, A. (2012). Providing support for newly qualified practitioners in Scotland. *Nursing Standard.* **27** (2), 33–36.

Johns, C. (1994). Nuances of reflection. *Journal of Clinical Nursing.* **3**, 71–75.

Knowles, M.S. (1975). *Self-Directed Learning. A Guide for Learners and Teachers.* Englewood Cliffs: Prentice Hall/Cambridge.

Kolb, D. A. (1984). *Experiential Learning: Experience as the Source of Learning and Development.* New Jersey: Prentice-Hall.

Lawson, S., Morris, R. & Hearle, D. (2014). A continuous, dynamic and strategic journey. *Occupational Therapy News.* **22** (5), 34.

Legare, F., Borduas, F., MacLeod, A., Sketeris, I., Campbell, B. & Jacques, A. (2011). Partnerships for knowledge translation and exchange in the context of continuing professional development. *Journal of Continuing Education in the Health Professions.* **33** (3), 181–87.

Lloyd, B., Pfeiffer, D., Dominish, J., Reading, G., Schmidt, D., and McCluskey, A. (2014). The New South Wales allied workplace learning study: barriers and enablers to learning in the workplace. *BMC Health Services Research.* **14** (134), 1–17.

Maclean, F., Jones, D., Carin-Levy, G. & Hunter, H. (2013). Understanding twitter. *British Journal of Occupational Therapy.* **76** (6), 295–98.

Maslach, C., Schaufeli, W. B. & Leiter, M. (2001). Job burnout. *Annual Review of Psychology.* **52**, 397–422.

Mathers, N., Mitchell, C. & Hunn, A. (2012). *A Study to Assess the Impact of Continuing Professional Development (CPD) on Doctors' Performance and Patient/Service Outcomes for the GMC.* http://www.gmc-uk.org/A_study_to_assess_the_impact_of_continuing_professional_development__CPD__on_doctors__performance_and_patient_service_outcomes_for_the_GMC_51707533.pdf (Accessed 25 April 2015).

McClelland, D.C. (1985). How motives, skills and values determine what people do. *American Psychologist.* **40**, 812–25.

Moon, J.A. (2004a). *A Handbook of Reflective and Experiential Learning: Theory and Practice.* London: RoutledgeFalmer.

Moon, J.A. (2004b). *Resources for Reflective Learning.* http://perpustakaandeajulia.weebly.com/uploads/1/8/2/6/18261275/a_handbook_of_reflective_and_experiential_learning_-_theory_and_practice.pdf (Accessed 25 July 2015).

Moorley, C. & Chinn, T. (2015). Using social media for continuous professional development. *Journal of Advanced Nursing.* **71** (4), 713–17.

Morris, R., Salmon, T., Hearle., Leadbitter, A., Morris, M. & Mandizha-Walker, M. (2011). Creativity through appreciative inquiry: The development of a model for continuing professional development. *OT News.* **19** (6), 26–27.

National Advisory group on the Safety of Patients in England (NAGSPE) (2013). *A promise to learn – a commitment to act: Improving the Safety of Patients in England.* London. Williams Lea. https://www.gov.uk/government/uploads/system/uploads/attachment_data/file/226703/Berwick_Report.pdf (Accessed 27 April 2015).

National Institute of Care and Excellence (NICE) (2015). *Glossary.* https://www.nice.org.uk/glossary?letter=q (Accessed 16 April 2015).

National Leadership and Innovation Agency for Healthcare (NLIAH) (2010). *Framework for Advanced Nursing, Midwifery and Allied Health Professional Practice in Wales.* http://www.wales.nhs.uk/sitesplus/documents/829/NLIAH%20Advanced%20Practice%20Framework.pdf (Accessed 25 April 2015).

NHS Employers (2013). *HR and Social Media in the NHS 2013 The Essential Guide for HR Directors and Managers.* http://www.nhsemployers.org/case-studies-and-resources/2013/01/hr-and-social-media-in-the-nhs (Accessed 25 April 2015).

NHS Staff Council (2009). *Improving Working Lives in the NHS – A Framework Developed by the NHS Staff Council.* London: NHS Employers.

O' Neill, E. (2004). *Professional Supervision: Myths, Culture and Structure.* RMA Publications: Co. Tipperary.

O'Sullivan, J. (2003). Unlocking the workforce potential: is support for effective continuing professional development the key? *Research in Post-Compulsory Education.* **8** (1), 107–22.

O'Sullivan, J. (2006). 'Continuing professional development' in R. Jones & F. Jenkins (eds) *Developing the Allied Health Professional.* Oxford: Radcliffe Publishing. 1–16.

Oxford Paperback Dictionary and Thesaurus (2007). 2nd edn. Oxford: Oxford University Press.

Parsloe, E. (2008). What is mentoring? MentorSET. http://www.mentorset.org.uk/what-is-mentoring.html (Accessed 9 October 2015).

Penman, M. (2014). Do We Have What it Takes? An Investigation into New Zealand Occupational Therapists' Readiness to be Self-directed Learners. http://oatd.org/oatd/record?record=handle%5C%3A10523%5C%2F4596 (Accessed 25 April 2015).

Rodgers, C. (2002). Seeing student learning: Teacher change and the role of reflection. *Harvard Educational Review.* 72 (2), 230–53.

Royal College of Nursing (RCN) (2007). *Joint Statement on Continuing Professional Development for Health and Social Care Practitioners.* London: RCN.

Scally, G. & Donaldson, L.J. (1998). Clinical governance and the drive for quality improvement in the new NHS in England. *British Medical Journal.* 317 (7150), 61–65.

Schaufeli, W.B. & Bakker, A.B. (2004). Job demands, job resources, and their relationship with burnout and engagement: a multi-sample study. *Journal of Organizational Behavior.* 25, 293–315.

Schon, D.A. (1983). *The Reflective Practitioner: How Professionals Think in Action.* London: Temple Smith.

Simpson, M.R. (2009). Engagement at work: A review of the literature. *International Journal of Nursing Studies.* **46** (7), 1012–24.

Skills for Care (2012). *The Social Work ASYE – A 'mini guide' to the Assessed and Supported Year in Employment.* http://www.skillsforcare.org.uk/Document-library/Social-work/Support-and-assessment/ASYE-mini-guide-Jan-14.pdf (Accessed 25 July 2015).

Starey, N. (2001). *What is Clinical Governance?* http://www.medicine.ox.ac.uk/bandolier/painres/download/whatis/WhatisClinGov.pdf (Accessed 13 March 2014).

Straus, S.E., Tetroe, J., Graham, I. (2009). Defining knowledge translation. *Canadian Medical Association Journal.* **181** (3-4), 165–68.

Strong, J. (2009). 'Clinical supervision skills' in E.A.S. Duncan (ed) *Skills for Practice in Occupational Therapy.* London: Churchill Livingstone. 338–49.

Strong, J., Kavanagh, D., Wilson, J., Spence, S., Worrall, L. & Crow, N. (2003). Supervision practice for allied health professionals within a large mental health service: Exploring the phenomenon. *The Clinical Supervisor.* **22** (1), 191–210.

The British Association of Social Workers (BASW) (2015). *Professional Capabilities Framework.* https://www.basw.co.uk/resource/?id=1137 (Accessed 02 October 2015).

Treseder, R. (2012). 'The Future of the Profession' in T. Polglase & R. Treseder (eds) *The Occupational Therapy Handbook: Practice Education.* Keswick: M&K Update Ltd. 131–48.

Van den Broeck, A., Vansteenkiste, M., DeWitte, H. & Lens, W. (2008). Explaining the relationships between job characteristics, burnout and engagement. *Work and Stress.* **22** (3), 277–94.

VARK Questionnaire (2015). http://vark-learn.com/the-vark-questionnaire/ (Accessed 12 March 2015).

Waite, M. & Keenan, J. (2010). *CPD for Non-Medical Prescribers: A Practical Guide.* Chichester: Wiley Blackwell.

World Health Organisation (WHO) (2006). *Quality of Care: A process for making strategic choices in health systems.* Geneva: WHO.

Youngstrom, M. J. (2009). 'Supervision' in E.B. Crepeau, S.E. Cohn, E.S. Boyt & B.A. Shelle (eds) *Willard & Spackman's Occupational Therapy.* 11th edn. Philadelphia: Wolters Kluwer, Lippincott, Williams & Wilkins. 929–48.

Index